ONE WORLD—*Many Men*

One of the most important facts about human beings is that they are not all alike. Yet if we are to survive, we must live in a world composed not only of differing individuals, but of differing groups. And if we are to adjust ourselves to such a world, we must understand what such differences mean, how they arise, how lasting they are likely to be and which of them may determine our individual and group destinies. In particular, we must know what differences are inborn and permanent and which result from upbringing and education.

In this revised and expanded edition of an important and illuminating book, Professors Dunn and Dobzhansky analyze the facts of heredity and present the case of "nature" and "nurture" in clear, simple, thoroughly scientific terms. Looking behind the external features of animals, plants and men, they describe the exact mechanism which governs heredity. They discuss in detail the questions of how particular genes or combinations of genes are likely to increase, decrease or remain stationary, and what significance these ideas have for the society of today and tomorrow. The authors have selected examples from contemporary events to illustrate the fallacies of various racial theories.

MENTOR and SIGNET Books
of Related Interest

HEREDITY, RACE
AND
SOCIETY

L. C. Dunn *and*
Th Dobzhansky

Revised and Enlarged Edition

A MENTOR BOOK from
NEW AMERICAN LIBRARY
TIMES MIRROR
New York and Toronto
The New English Library Limited, London

CONTENTS

67710

1. Human Differences

HUMAN BEINGS are not all alike. From the beginning of the record and to this day there have always been big men and small men, strong men and weak men, wise men and fools. To some people music is the source of greatest pleasure, to others it is just unnecessary noise; some people draw easily and well, others can not sketch a simple figure; some enjoy intense activity and violent exercise, others prefer repose and meditation. In any large group of persons you will find some with good eyesight, others with poor, some will be color-blind or unable to taste or smell some particular substance; and if you examine their facial features or their finger patterns, you will find that actually no two persons are alike. One thing you can be sure of is that the next man you meet will be different from the last, and if you visit a new country you will certainly find different customs and ways of doing things.

Differences among men are important because they underlie the conflicts which have shaken the world since history began. But human diversity is also responsible for the great material and cultural progress of mankind. If you do not believe that it takes all kinds of people to make our kind of world, just try to imagine its opposite, a world in which all men are alike. Could such a world have farms and factories, automobiles and airplanes, newspapers and symphony orchestras, poetry and scientific research?

That human diversity leads to both bad and good results should make us pause and consider that it is not the differences themselves which instigate strife and conflicts but rather our way of regarding them. Human differences often seem so important that we forget that, after all, men are fundamentally very similar to each other. American democracy is based on the idea that all men are born equal before the law. Yet although they have equal rights they are assuredly not all alike. And perhaps the most precious right of each man is to have his unique personality respected by others, to be allowed to be different from his fellows.

The problem we must face is how to live in a world in which persons and groups differ in political opinions, in moral and religious beliefs, and in all kinds of tastes and predilections. To adapt ourselves to such a world, we must understand what human differences mean, how they arise, how lasting they may be, and whether we may be able to control them.

For example, one of the ways in which men differ sharply from each other without knowing it is in their ability to taste a chemical substance known as phenyl-thio-carbamide (PTC for short). To about 70 per cent of Americans, a weak solution of this substance has an intensely bitter taste; to the other 30 per cent it is almost tasteless. This difference is inherited, and it is not known to be influenced by any changes in the environment. Now imagine that PTC is used as a disinfectant in drinking water in a town in which no one has heard of the difference between "tasters" and "taste blinds." When the first complaints of bad-tasting drinking water are received an inspector is sent to investigate. The inspector, who is taste-blind, reports that he can't see what all the fuss is about and ascribes the complaints to prejudice or "trouble-making." This does not make the water taste any better to those who had complained, and gradually two opposed parties emerge, a pro-PTC and an anti-PTC. An election puts in the antis, who have a 70 per cent majority, and disinfection with PTC is discontinued.

To the 30 per cent who are pro-PTC (because they can't taste it) the whole procedure has been unreasonable in the extreme. Because of an obstinate majority they have been deprived of protection against infection. If they feel strongly enough about this they may attempt to subvert the rule of the majority. The majority then may be tempted to use police-state methods to suppress the rebellious minority.

In this case the fact that the majority was right was due to the biological accident that the hereditary factor for taste blindness is less common than its alternative. Although PTC is not used as a disinfectant, and the above events are not known to have happened, there is no doubt that many human conflicts arise because inborn differences are ascribed to prejudice and vice versa.

Different or Superior?

All peoples have recognized the diversity of human individuals. Most often they have taken it for granted that physical and mental differences are inborn, inherited, and unalterable. The Old Testament abounds in parables of predestination. It seems that there were always men destined to be kings and others to be the everlasting meek. How much the ancient Hebrews believed in the power of heredity must be plain to anyone who follows the biblical leaders and prophets to the places assigned to them by the ways in which they differed from their fellows.

It is only a step from the individual differences to group differences, and most peoples, primitive and civilized alike, are acutely conscious of their differences from other peoples. Just as the fear of competition with other individuals gives rise to pride and conceit, so too when we recognize how our family, tribe, or nation differs from others, then our fear and sense of insecurity give rise to group pride. It is because groups recognize and exalt the ways in which they differ from others that there have been in human history so many "chosen people," each having, because of its native virtues, an inside track to the favor of the true God.

Hitler believed that the Aryan-Nordic-German race was the only one endowed with a multitude of excellent qualities and with no bad ones. But do not credit Hitler with having invented national self-glorification; since time immemorial people everywhere have indulged in this. Consider, for example, the following excerpts from the epistle addressed in 1793 by Emperor Chien Lung of China to King George III of Britain in response to the latter's embassy proposing commercial relations between the two countries:

"You, O King, live beyond the confines of many seas; nevertheless, impelled by your humble desire to partake of the benefits of our civilization, you have dispatched a mission respectfully bearing your memorial. . . . If you assert that your reverence for Our Celestial Dynasty fills you with a desire to acquire our civilization, our ceremonies and code of laws differ so completely from your own that, even if your Envoy were able to acquire the rudiments of our civilization, you could not possibly transplant our manners and customs to your alien soil. . . . If I have commanded that the tribute offerings sent by you, O King, are to be accepted, this was solely in consideration for the spirit which prompted you to despatch them from afar. Our Dynasty's majestic virtue has penetrated into every country under Heaven, and kings of all nations have offered their costly tribute by land and sea. As your Ambassador can see for himself, we possess all things. I set no value on objects strange or ingenious, and have no use for your country's manufactures."

Does this sound ridiculous? No more so than the similar chatter of many Britishers and Americans about the superiority of "Anglo-Saxon civilization" over the "Unchanging East." Much effort has been expended to prove the superiority of the so-called Nordic race of Northwestern Europe, generally of course by Nordics or those who thought they were Nordics; just as similar claims that the cream of the Nordic race is to be found in the "Old American stock" are usually traceable to "Old Americans."

This sort of conceit is not confined to powerful or

aggressive nations. A beautiful work of an eminent Mexican modern painter has inscribed in it the words "Through *my* race will speak the Spirit." The reader may never have heard about the nomadic tribes of Kirghiz living in the mountains and deserts of central Asia. But one of us heard a gray-bearded Kirghizian patriarch expounding the conviction that the "heart" of the Kirghizian is superior to that of any other people: "And the heart is what really matters in men," he said with an air of finality.

The belief that the differences between men and races are inborn and unalterable is probably older and more widespread than the other view that human appearance and personality are formed entirely by the influences of the environment in which people live and by the training which they receive. Both extreme views are wrong, since it is known that many human traits, such as the character of our blood, whether we are taste-blind or not, the color of our eyes, and many other traits are inborn—they are determined very largely by heredity; while many others, including the diseases we get, the language we speak, the religion we profess, are determined not by heredity but by where we happened to be born, by our environment. A moment's thought will show us that between so-called "hereditary" and so-called "environmental" traits there is no hard and fast line. Both heredity and environment must of course be involved in the origin of every human characteristic. But our beliefs concerning which of these has a decisive influence on specific differences will determine our actions regarding them.

Democracy and Racism

Several solutions of the problem of human diversity have been advocated ever since the beginning of recorded history. One of the basic tenets of Christianity is that all men are sons of God and equal before God. Physical, mental, and cultural differences among men must then be considered superficial and relatively quite unimportant. Hence, Christianity and other great religions have always taught (no matter what they practiced) that mankind is one great family in which brotherhood should ultimately prevail.

An application of the above teachings to practical life and politics is the democratic idea which has grown and developed during almost two thousand years in Europe and more recently in America. Democracy accepts human diversity as a fact of experience, but nevertheless holds that all men have the same inalienable rights. Democratic society should, then, be adapted to the variable natures of its members. It would create such political, social, and economic arrangements as would furnish to each member the opportunities to develop the best potentialities of his personality and of his creative energies to the fullest possible extent. In so doing, democracy would take advantage of human diversity, and in fact preserve the unlikenesses.

To many people the religious and democratic solutions seem, however, impractical and unattractive. It is argued that all men are not born equal in ability or in capacity to develop the characteristics which are regarded as useful or pleasing. Now, if some humans are "well born" and others are endowed more sparingly, then they are not equal in worth, and perhaps should not presume to claim equality in rights either. This is especially true if human differences are fixed in biological heredity, and consequently are inevitable and unalterable. The fate of every individual is, according to this view, very largely fixed by the "Dice of Destiny" hidden in his hereditary endowment.

The doctrine of inherent inequality of men has been developed by many thinkers, starting with Plato in ancient Greece. More recently there was the Comte de Gobineau, a cultivated and intelligent French nobleman who about a century ago wrote a book called "Essay on the Inequality of Races." To Gobineau, the intellectual and emotional differences between the great white Nordic race and the inferior whites, yellows, and blacks were

clearly innate; although certain of the Latin whites—
French, Spanish, and Italian—whose blood had been
polluted by mixing with unworthy "lower races," were
bound to decay. This theory of innate differences by
which groups of men could be classified into superior
and inferior races found ready support, particularly in
Germany, where it was expounded among others by the
"renegade Englishman," Houston Chamberlain, whose
writings underlay the race myths of the Nazis. There was
even a good scientist, Max Müller, who on an unlucky
day used the words "Aryan race" to describe peoples
who spoke a certain group of languages. Müller soon
recognized his mistake, for differences in speech need not
have anything to do with biological racial differences.
But while this mistake died early in science, it lived in
politics, and thus there arose, truly out of talk alone, an
imaginary creature, Aryan Man, which became one of
the Nazi gods.

It wasn't long before the Aryan and Nordic race theories found support in England and America. In this
country we had such books as Madison Grant's "Passing
of the Great Race," and Lothrop Stoddard's "Rising
Tide of Color" to warn us that the Melting Pot is about
to ruin beyond repair the American breed of man. Scare
propaganda of this sort became widespread and gained
some influence on public opinion, especially in the
decades preceding and following the First World War.
It probably had political repercussions in the enactment
of the immigration laws and in the temporary ascend-
ance of isolationism in the U.S.A. A strong popular
revulsion against racism set in, however, when Hitler
came to power in Germany and used the alleged superiority of the Nordic race and similar notions to justify
military aggression and the extermination of millions
of innocent victims in concentration camps.

Scientific Study of Human Diversity

Until recently the religious and political solutions of
the problem of human diversity had not sought any

"scientific" foundation or vindication. Now, however, you hear people say "There ought to be a scientific solution," or "Science ought to be able to tell us how to live in a world where these human differences keep stirring up conflicts." And indeed, attempts have been made to examine scientifically the questions about human differences. Unfortunately, many of these attempts failed because scientists, like all other men, often succumb to the temptation to prove some particular view or to reinforce some preconceived ideas about human affairs.

Francis Galton, a versatile English scientist, who was a younger contemporary and a relative of Darwin, propounded the view that most human differences are innate, due, in his words, to Nature rather than to Nurture. Galton was convinced that the English propertied and governing classes were a repository of virtually all that is biologically precious in the English nation and possibly in mankind. He wrote: "By natural ability . . . I mean a nature which, when left to itself, will, urged by an inherent stimulus, climb the path that leads to eminence, and has strength to reach the summit—one which, if hindered or thwarted, will fret and strive until the hindrance is overcome, and it is again free to follow its labor-loving instinct. It is almost a contradiction in terms to doubt such men will generally become eminent. On the other hand, there is plenty of evidence in this volume to show that few have won high reputations without possessing these peculiar gifts. It follows that the men who achieve eminence, and those who are naturally capable, are, to a large extent, identical. I have shown that social hindrances cannot impede men of high ability from becoming eminent. I shall now maintain that social advantages are incompetent to give that status to a man of moderate ability."

How different from Galton's is the view of H. J. Muller, one of the leading modern biologists: "It could at least as well be maintained that the dominant classes tend to have the genetic equipment which would be least desirable in a well-ordered social system, since they have been selected chiefly on the basis of predatory, rather than truly constructive behavior. The 'respectable' captain of industry, military leader or politician, and the successful gangster are psychologically not so far apart. The high-minded, the scrupulous, the idealistic, the generous and those who are too intelligent to wish to confine their interests to their personal monetary success, these are apt to be left behind in the present-day battle."

Galton pointed out that it should be possible to improve the human stock in the same way in which farm livestock has been improved, that is, breeding from the best. This would require some social control over human marriage and reproduction, and to the study of such ways of improving the human race Galton gave the name "Eugenics," which means being well born. As originally stated by Galton it was intended "to give to the more suitable races or strains of blood a better chance of prevailing speedily over the less suitable than they otherwise would have had." As we have seen, the socially eminent and financially successful are, in Galton's view, largely identical with the biologically "suitable." From "the more suitable races" it is not a very far cry to the "great race" or the "master race." In its emphasis on human inequalities and its assumption that they are fixed by birth, eugenics tended to deflect attention from those individual and social conditions which could be remedied to those for which the only cure is to prevent their birth. It must be admitted that this is indeed a gentler doctrine than the extermination recommended (and practiced) by the Nazis. Yet, it is an interesting fact that in the United States some of the most ardent eugenists were also adherents of the myth of Nordic and white superiority.

The kind of solution proposed by Gobineau and his followers assumed that innate differences must give rise to fixed social, political, economic, and cultural inequalities. The solution, by and large, was that all men should recognize and conform to a natural hierarchy or order among races and persons extending from high to low and good to bad. It is not surprising that writers with a desire to create such categories should have been swayed by prejudice and self-interest.

In general, solutions to such problems as what to do about inborn differences among men can arise only out of the knowledge and understanding which it is the function of science to provide. Powers over human life as great as those required to put a eugenical program into effect can be entrusted only to a society in which social and economic equality of individuals and groups is guaranteed and protected in positive ways. The best protection is the will and knowledge of the people and it is a fundamental obligation of science to acquaint them with the biological facts necessary for understanding human likenesses and differences. That will be the aim of this little book. We shall try to state the facts of heredity as simply as we can, so that those with no previous acquaintance with the subject can understand its basic ideas and appraise some of the evidence upon which the ideas rest. In doing this it will be necessary to explain what heredity is and how it operates when the likenesses and differences of the parents are distributed amongst their children in accordance with definite rules. These rules, known as Mendel's laws, depend upon the peculiar way in which the sex cells, egg and sperm, of man, animals, and most plants are formed and combine to produce the offspring; and the pertinent facts of sexual reproduction will thus be stated at the outset.

We then ask the old question "Is it nature or nurture, heredity or environment, or is it some combination of these that is responsible for human differences?" Here we have new evidence to consider from the fascinating studies of twins which in recent years have thrown much new light on this question. There follows a simple description of the actual method and mechanism by which individual hereditary differences are transmitted, and this leads of course to a subject of major interest: how these individual differences behave in large groups such as races. Here we have found it possible to discuss in a purely scientific way such "fighting questions" as whether race differences are absolute or relative, and what the prospects are for the disappearance or increase of racial differences.

We may as well state at the outset that we are not seeking to persuade anyone of the virtues of any type, class, or breed of man, or of any special political or economic order of society. As biologists we view human differences as facts which call for understanding and interpretation, not as qualities to be either condemned or praised. In fact, in describing groups of men in biological terms, we do not recognize categories defined as "good" or "bad," "superior" or "inferior." These general categories are statements of opinion; to have any meaning as facts they would have to be accompanied by specific statements such as "Most Negroes are superior to most whites in their resistance to malaria," or "Most whites are superior to most Negroes in their resistance to tuberculosis." Statements about the superiority of one group over another in native intelligence are usually made from the standpoint and for the purpose of one of the groups, under which the other must always be at a disadvantage.

2. Nature and Nurture

WHY ARE PEOPLE different one from another? Why aren't we all alike? Men have been asking this question for hundreds of years, and the answers that have been given to it boil down to two. First, people are different because food, climate, upbringing, education, income—in short, the physical and cultural surroundings—are not the same for all. People differ because their environments differ. Second, we come from different parents, different families, stocks and races of men: our heredities differ. These two great forces, environment and heredity, form our bodies, minds, and characters. Galton long ago called these forces nurture (the conditions of life) and nature (inborn, inherited).

Much time has been spent in argument about the relative importance of nature and nurture. Probably tens of thousands of hours have been used up by students preparing for debates on: "Resolved, that Heredity is more important than Environment." Although it would be too harsh to say that these hours have been wasted, nevertheless a little thought will show that the question asked in that form has not much meaning. We can not take away from any human being either his heredity or his environment. We come into the world as a bundle of possibilities bequeathed to us by our parents and other ancestors. Our nurture comes from the world about us. What happens to the nurture that comes in depends, however, on the nature that receives it. Food is useless to us without digestive organs that convert it into the living substance which is us, and words of wisdom are of no avail without a brain to heed and retain them. On the other hand, inherited possibilities would never become actualities without the means by which they may grow and develop. Nature and nurture are so obviously necessary and inseparable that the important question is not which is more important but rather how together they determine our qualities.

Sexual Reproduction

All our heredity, our nature, is transmitted to us from our parents through tiny cells which connect our living substance with that of our forebears. Each human being takes its origin from the union of two of these bits of living matter, an egg from the mother which has been fertilized by a single sperm from the father. The egg is a tiny sphere hardly visible to the naked eye; it has been estimated that twenty million human eggs would weigh about one ounce. A sperm is visible only with the aid of a microscope, and its volume is about eighty-five thousand times smaller than that of an egg. Furthermore, a sperm is quite different from an egg in appearance, being shaped like a thread inflated at one end to form a "head." Some idea of the sizes of these living links between the generations has been given by an eminent American biologist, H. J. Muller, who has calculated that if we could collect together all the eggs from which the present human population of the earth has sprung—approximately two and a half billions of them—they would all occupy the volume of less than a gallon. The sperm cells—two and a half billions of them —would occupy the space of half an aspirin tablet.

We inherit our natures about equally from both parents, that is, father and mother are equally important in the transmission of heredity. And yet, the male and the female sex cells are, as we have seen, extremely different in size and in appearance and structure as well. How can such different vehicles convey the same hereditary traits? Already in the nineteenth century some biologists saw that the only reasonable solution of this paradox is to suppose that it is not the sex cell as a whole but some particular bit of it, alike in both sexes, which is chiefly concerned with heredity. Indeed, a careful study of the sex cells under strong microscopes showed that one part is similar in eggs and sperms. These similar parts are the nuclei of the sex cells, or, more precisely, the chromosomes in the nuclei. Each human egg and each sperm contains twenty-four chromosomes, which are tiny bits of a living substance which can be stained with certain dyes. A theory was put forward at the turn of the century that heredity is transmitted through the chromosomes. This chromosome theory of heredity has been fully confirmed by much further evidence discovered in the present century.

The chromosomes occupy a considerable fraction of the volume of the sperm, but only a tiny fraction of the volume of the egg. The combined volumes of the chromosomes in the 2,500,000,000 sperms and in the equal number of egg cells from which the human beings now living have sprung would add up to less bulk than an aspirin tablet. And yet, this minute amount of substance contained the heredity of the whole human race!

The life of a new individual is kindled when a sperm fertilizes an egg. Fertilization consists in fusion of the nucleus of the sperm with that of an egg. The fertilized egg proceeds then to divide into two, four, eight, and finally billions of cells which compose the adult body. Each cell receives, by division, a nucleus identical with that of the fertilized egg. The heredity received from the parents is, thus, present in every cell of the child.

The developing body grows very rapidly at first and then more slowly. An adult body weighs about fifty billion times as much as a fertilized egg. Where does the material for this stupendous increase come from? The answer is not far to seek: the material is taken in from the environment. At first it is the nutriment which comes to the unborn child through the mother's blood, and then from the food which we ourselves consume. Quite literally, the material which is "ourselves" is derived from the neighborhood grocery store. But food does not become a part of the living body except through a complex process of digestion and assimilation. It is the heredity of the assimilating organism which transforms the nutriment taken from the outside into a likeness of that organism and of its ancestors.

Heredity and Environment

By and large, the materials which enter our bodies are pretty much the same for every human—so much water, so much oxygen, so much mineral, protein, carbohydrate and other foods. This is almost literally true for unborn children which are nourished by the mother's blood, since human blood has a very constant composition. And yet different heredities transform this same material into different forms, and different individuals result. Consider that the environment is roughly the same for brothers and sisters reared in the same household. Nothing is more certain, however, than that brothers and sisters often, perhaps generally, respond in different ways to the same environment. A brother gets the curly hair that a sister so ardently desires. Moreover he has an allergy to the cats on which the sister dotes. Eggs "do not agree" with her while he wants them twice a day. One hums melodies from babyhood while the other is tone deaf and can not carry a simple tune.

Negroes have been living in the United States almost as long as whites, yet whites and blacks have not, in the common environment, come to resemble each other in skin color. We know that the lighter color of some people classed as Negroes is due not to nurture or climate, but to white ancestors. In Africa, similarly, white men retain their skin color after many generations of residence. Looked at superficially, it may seem that nature dominates nurture, because different natures transform a similar nurture into different shapes, and different nurtures are transformed by similar natures into roughly similar shapes. But a little consideration will show that all that such a statement means is that if an environment is at all suitable for human life, a baby either grows to be a man or does not live at all. What we really want to know is how different could individuals with similiar heredities become in different environments, and how great are the differences which individuals with different heredities may be expected to display in the same environment.

The skin colors in Negroes and whites differ doubtless by nature. But observe the skin colors of enthusiastic bathers on beaches in California or Florida, or for that matter near New York in late summer. Some are as dark as Negroes, or at least as mulattoes. Yet, some of these dark-skinned fellows become quite pale after spending a long winter in a city apartment. Such changes in the skin color are evidently due to environment and not to heredity. The upshot is, however, that, strange as it may seem, a "black" and "white" sometimes have very nearly the same skin colors. The statement that Negroes and whites differ in skin color proves to be inaccurate, or at least incomplete. We really should say that they differ in the skin color in some environments but not in others. It would be even better to say that among people called "white" there are some individuals who do not develop much color in the skin regardless of exposure to sunlight, some who have little or no color without exposure but a strong coloration after a long exposure to sunlight, and finally some whose skins are more or less swarthy with or without sunlight. Negroes have dark skins in all known environments.

What Is Heredity?

When you hear it said of somebody that he has inherited a house and a bank account, you know that a certain building and a certain legal document have been transferred from one person to another. This obviously can not be the meaning of the statement that a man has inherited his eye color from his father and his disposition from his mother. Biological heredity is transmitted through sex cells, which have no eyes in them and no definable disposition. It is not the eye color or other "traits" that are inherited, but something within the sex cells which determines how a living individual will react to various environments. In some families children are born who in spite of adequate feeding and care never grow to be tall. Members of other families grow tall and strong with little care. These facts do not contradict the opinion of medical authorities that nutrition, exercise and health conditions influence the growth and physical development of children. We can say that stature is inherited; it is more accurate to say that stature depends upon heredity as well as upon environment. Each heredity responds to each environment by producing a certain stature.

Some people can not retain and utilize sugars which they get in their food; instead, the sugars are expelled in the urine. These people are diabetics, and some forms of this disease are hereditary. About three decades ago it was discovered that injections of a drug called insulin relieve promptly the attacks of diabetes. The injections do not cure the cause of the illness itself, and the attacks recur unless injections are made at proper intervals. If given regular injections a diabetic may lead a normal existence. A normal body prepares its own insulin; the heredity of a diabetic makes his body incapable of preparing insulin; but if insulin is supplied from outside, the acute disorder called diabetes fails to appear. You may not suspect that your friend has a diabetic heredity if he creates for himself an artificial environment containing insulin.

Heredity Is Not Destiny

Some people speak and write about heredity as though it were some implacable destiny the decisions of which can not be appealed. Such a hopeless and defeatist view is not necessary if we realize that heredity determines the responses of the person to the environment and not the presence or absence of this or that trait as such. We can not change the heredity with which we were born, but in at least some cases we can choose an environment to which our heredity will respond most favorably. Those who like dark skin color take sun baths or apply the color out of a bottle. The diabetics use insulin. White ladies with straight hair have it "permanently" waved, and Negro ladies have theirs straightened. To be sure, no ointments, drugs, or other treatments are known for many heredities. They may be discovered in the future, even as the insulin treatment of diabetes has recently been discovered.

This certainly does not solve the nature-nurture problem. The fact remains that there are many different environments, many different heredities, and that people differ from one another in many ways. We want to know to what extent the observed differences between men are due to the existing variety of environments and of heredities. We ought to be able to recognize as "environmental" those differences which appear when persons of the same heredity are exposed to different environments. Unfortunately, it is not easy to find people of the same heredity. We know that even members of the same family, brothers and sisters, differ from each other in heredity. Even small hereditary differences between people may make big differences when the environment is changed, especially in the mental reactions which are so important and interesting to us. For example, good eyesight may be a great advantage, and even a small defect in vision uncorrected by glasses may become a great handicap in studying.

To get reliable information on heredity and environment we ought to be able to do with humans what experimental biologists have done with some plants. For example, dandelion plants have been divided into halves, one half of each plant being transplanted to a mountain top and the other left in the valley. The two halves of each plant have exactly similar heredities, and they develop into new whole plants being reared under different conditions. The differences in size, form, number of leaves, length of stem and roots which come to distinguish these plants may thus be traced directly to specified environmental conditions. Such knowledge is very useful, and would be especially important for human beings.

Twins

In humans, obviously, it is not possible to make experiments of this kind deliberately, but luckily, such experiments happen once in a while by accident. These accidents are called "identical twins." In one birth out of about each 87, more than one baby is born. In a great majority of these cases two babies are born, rarely there are three, that is triplets (about one in 7,400 births), and still more rarely there are four (about one in 636,-000 births). Quintuplets and sextuplets are extremely rare but not so rare as is popularly believed, since some sixty cases of quintuplets are recorded and even six cases of sextuplets.

Of the twins born, about one quarter are identical twins, and it is easy to understand why these are so interesting and useful for answering questions about heredity and environment. Ordinary twins are merely a pair of babies who happen to be born at the same time. They come from two separate eggs and show the same hereditary differences as ordinary brothers and sisters. Identical twins on the other hand are like the two halves of the plant that was cut, for these twins arise when a single fertilized egg, by some accident, gets split into two parts early in development, and each part grows into a separate and complete individual. Since these individuals have the same heredity, any differences between them must be due to environment, to nurture. This should help us to assess the part played by environment in producing differences among humans.

Identical twins had attracted the attention of laymen as well as of biologists before their manner of origin was known, just because they are so nearly identical in appearance. They are always of the same sex, same complexion, eye color, hair form and blood type, and are similar in height and build. They tend to make similar records at school and to resemble each other mentally and spiritually as well. You may say, of course, that these similarities are due to the similarity in their environments before and usually after birth; but you must remember that similarity of environments does not make ordinary twins, the "two-egg" variety alike. Two-egg twins may be and often are quite unlike. In about half the cases they are of opposite sex. Regardless of sex, one may be blond, the other brunet; one tall, the other short, etc. These characters are hereditary, and environmental similarity does not extinguish differences in them. We must, therefore, conclude that the similarity in appearance of identical twins is due to their identical heredity as well as to like environment.

As "one-egg" twins grow older some differences between them begin to appear. One may gain weight a little faster than the other; one may come to learn a little more easily, develop a "shorter temper" or otherwise depart from the other. Indeed, in some respects they may be slightly different at birth, one often being right-handed, the other left-handed. Some of these differences, appearing before as well as after birth, can be traced to environment. Thus if one gets measles and the other escapes (which rarely happens), the eyesight of one may be weakened and learning speed thereby lessened. We begin to see how particular differences between twins might be traceable to particular environmental factors; how, in other words, we could, by studying one-egg twins, estimate the relative influence of heredity and environment upon particular characters. This is possible when one-egg twins are separated at birth and adopted by families living under different conditions. This is the nearest approach possible in man to the ideal experiment in which a single individual is divided into two parts, each of which is transplanted to a different environment.

One-egg twins reared apart have been studied by several scientists, beginning with Galton in the nineteenth century, but it remained for the team of H. H. Newman (a biologist), F. N. Freeman (a psychologist) and K. J. Holzinger (a statistician) of the University of Chicago to make the most thoroughgoing study of such twins. After some fifteen years of work they found and studied twenty pairs of one-egg twins of which the members had been separated in infancy. For comparison they studied fifty pairs of one-egg twins which had been reared together and fifty pairs of two-egg (but same-sexed) twins reared together. From comparison of members of all of these twin pairs in physical and mental traits they sought to discover first, to what extent and in what traits the members of one-egg pairs were more alike than the members of two-egg pairs, and second—to what extent and in what traits the differences in one-egg twins were increased when their environments were different. Similar studies have been made by a number of other investigators working in different countries. The results agree in all important respects.

Physical Traits in Twins

Newman, Freeman, and Holzinger made careful measurements and observations on a variety of physical characters (height, weight, head shape, fingerprints, etc.) in their twins. They also submitted them to a series of psychological tests designed to measure their intelligence, personality, and achievement. A part of their results is summarized in the following table, which gives the average differences between the twins of a pair in various traits:

AVERAGE DIFFERENCES BETWEEN MEMBERS OF TWIN-PAIRS

	One-Egg Twins Reared Together	One-Egg Twins Reared Apart	Two-Egg Twins Reared Together
Standing height (in centimeters)	1.6	1.8	4.4
Weight (in lbs.)	4.0	9.9	10.0
Head length (in millimeters)	2.6	2.2	6.2
Head width (in millimeters)	2.2	2.8	4.2
Intelligence Quotient (Binet)	5.3	8.2	9.9
Stanford Achievement (in months)	6.4	16.3	11.6

It can be seen that the one-egg twins are, regardless of whether they were reared together or apart, more nearly similar in body height than are the two-egg twins. The average difference in height amounts to 1.6 cm. in the one-egg twins reared together, and to 1.8 cm. when the twins are reared apart. The two-egg twins, although reared together, differed appreciably more— 4.4 cm. The same is true for the length and width of the head, the number of finger ridges, and some other traits. In fact, the average difference in head length happens to be even slightly less in the one-egg twins reared apart than in those reared together. But notice that the one-egg twins reared apart differed in weight about as much as the two-egg twins, and much more than the one-egg twins reared together.

What do these observations mean? Remember that the one-egg twins have similar heredities, regardless of whether they are reared together or apart. Two-egg twins differ in heredity as much as do brothers and sisters born at different times. Therefore, the greater differences found between two-egg as compared with one-egg twins can be safely ascribed to heredity. On the other hand, when the twins reared apart differ on the average more than do twins reared together, it is the environment which is responsible. We can see that different traits are influenced to different extents by heredity and by environment. In physical features, such as eye and hair color, head shape, or height, one-egg twins remained extremely similar even when separated at birth and brought up in different environments. But one-egg twins may become rather different in weight. Environment can modify the weight of a person relatively more easily than it can modify his height or his head shape. But it does not follow that heredity has nothing to do with one's weight. Surely, you know persons who find it difficult to "keep their weight down" despite keeping themselves on "reducing" diets, and other persons who can not gain much weight even on "fattening" foods.

Retention of great similarities amongst separated one-egg twins produced some dramatic situations. A girl of sixteen named Edith was accosted by a young man: "Hello, Fay, how do you happen to be so far from home?" Suspecting an attempt at flirtation, Edith repulsed the young man. But he was a persistent young man who trusted his memory for faces, so in another city he found the real Fay and arranged for her to go and see Edith. Edith met her and was, as she said, "shocked to see myself getting off the train." These girls proved to be one-egg twins separated at birth and adopted by different families.

Mental Traits and Achievement in Twins

There is also the story of identical twin brothers, both of whom became, during World War II, generals in the U.S. Air Force, although they had not served in the same military units and had made their careers independently. Can one conclude from this instance that it was the hereditary endowment of these men which was responsible for their similar achievements in the same field of activity? Such a conclusion is quite unwarranted. It is possible that the twin brother of some other general still serves as a sergeant, or that he has become tired of army life altogether.

Newman, Freeman, and Holzinger compared the mental abilities of twins by means of various "intelligence tests." On one of these I.Q. tests (Binet's) the average difference between one-egg twins reared together amounted to 5.3 "points," but when they were reared apart the difference increased to 8.2 "points." Two-egg twins reared together showed an average difference of 9.9 "points." It follows that mental ability, though undoubtedly influenced by heredity, is less fixed and more liable to modification by environment than most physical traits. In different achievement tests, supposedly measuring educational performance, the role of environment proved to be greater still. The Stanford achievement test showed the average difference between one-egg twins reared apart to be even greater than that between two-egg twins reared together. In spelling, the one-egg twins were more alike than the two-egg ones, while in arithmetic environment was much more important. In tests of motor ability and emotional balance, environment assumed the major role, more than half of the differences between twins being due to experience, training, and other environmental factors and less than half to heredity.

It must also be pointed out that the environments of the separated twins studied by Newman, Freeman and Holzinger were not very different. The twins were reared in the same country and generally in a similar class of society and exposed to the same educational system. We do not know how different the twins might have been if one of them were to grow up, say, in a city slum and the other in surroundings of comfort and refinement; or else, if one were to grow up in an American town and the other in a tribe of Asiatic nomads.

No observations of identical twins reared apart in such sharply different environments have so far been made. Instead, Snyder and Lehmann studied nineteen pairs of identical twins and tried to evaluate as carefully as possible the magnitude of the differences between the social environments and between the educational opportunities of the members of each pair of twins. The I.Q.'s of these twins were then measured, and attempts were made to relate them to the conditions in which the twins were reared. Some quite considerable differences between the members of the same twin pairs were found. Thus, one twin scored 24 I.Q. "points" above his co-twin, in another pair the difference between the co-twins amounted to 19 "points," in still another to 17 "points," etc. In other twin pairs, however, both twins were very much alike, differing in just one or a few I.Q. "points." Now, it turned out that in the twin pairs in which one of the twins scored appreciably higher than his co-twin, the superior twin had been raised and educated in a markedly superior environment. Conversely, when the environments of the twins were more nearly similar their I.Q. scores were also rather close. In fact, in three cases, the twin whose environment was rated as slightly superior had an I.Q. one or two points *below* his co-twin. This shows that our evaluation of the environment as "superior" or "inferior" is subject to error; furthermore, the I.Q. score of the same person may vary by a few points up or down if the test is administered repeatedly.

Is Crime Inherited?

Several investigators in different countries (United States, Holland, Germany) combed prisons for members of twin pairs among the inmates. When a twin was found efforts were made to locate his co-twin brother and to determine whether the latter did or did not have a criminal record. A total of 111 pairs of identical twins were investigated, and in 80 cases both co-twins were found to have had criminal records of various kinds. Among the same number (111 pairs) of two-egg twins, only 38 pairs consisted of co-twins both of whom had criminal records, while in the remaining 73 pairs one of the twins was convicted for some crime while his co-twin was not known to have broken any law. Clearly, then, one-egg twins are more often similar in having criminal records than are two-egg twins.

What, however, do these facts mean? One of the investigators described his findings in a book entitled *Crime as Destiny*. To him and to some others, the "coincidences in the lives of identical twins mean that heredity has the inevitability of fate." Some shocked proponents of the importance of the evironment declared that there must be something wrong with the data, since everybody knows that crime is a social phenomenon, and, as a consequence, it just cannot be due to heredity.

It may nevertheless be useful to restrain one's excitement and to look at the data once more dispassionately. Indeed, there is nothing in the observations to show that the individuals who committed crimes, and were caught at it, would have done so had they been brought up differently. Perhaps some of them would have become pillars of society, or judges and lawyers, instead of defendants and convicts. Even in the environments in which they actually lived, some identical twin brothers of the criminals appeared to be law-abiding citizens. Therefore their heredities did not necessarily predestine them to careers of crime. Nor is there anything to show that some of those who are reputed to be virtuous and respectable would not have gone astray had they lived in environments conducive to crime. All the data do show is, then, that people with similar heredities tend to react more similarly than do people with different heredities.

Foster Children

The dependence of mental traits on both heredity and environment can also be demonstrated by studies on foster children. When children are distributed to foster homes, it is unavoidable that some of them will be placed in more and others in less favorable environments. One can, then, compare the intelligence and other traits in children who grow up in different environments. Such comparisons are especially interesting if, as often happens, the families which take foster children also have children of their own. Suppose, for the sake of argument, that the intelligence of a growing child is determined solely by his environment. The intelligence of foster children should then be proportional to that of "own" children of the adopting families. If, on the contrary, intelligence were due to heredity alone, there would be no consistent relationship between the intelligence test scores of foster and of own children. The actual situation is intermediate between these extremes. Foster children show higher I.Q.'s in homes in which own children have higher I.Q.'s, and vice versa. This attests to the importance of the environment. But this is not the whole story. In the most favorable foster homes foster children average lower in performance than do own children; in the less favored families foster children show, on the contrary, an average performance superior to own children. This shows the presence of a hereditary component in the development of the qualities which the I.Q. tests measure.

Perhaps it will help to summarize the current views about the Nature-Nurture problem to employ an allegory, which however must not be pushed too far or taken too literally. In the formation of each human trait there is a kind of lock-and-key arrangement between the inborn Nature and the surrounding Nurture. Nature provides a great variety of locks, and Nurture many different keys. Each trait has its own class of locks and will respond to a limited number of keys. Some locks do not at present respond to any keys provided by the existing variety of environments. Thus, some mental defectives do not benefit by any kind of advanced education; but only a few years ago diabetics also did not respond to any of the treatments which had been tried. It took a newly invented key, insulin, to fit that peculiar lock. The lock by which "criminal behavior" is regulated is in some persons so set that it does not easily yield to the ordinary keys presented by poverty, defective education, and other bad surroundings. But in other persons the "criminal behavior" locks open with any one of these keys. Knowing that heredity determines only responses to environments but not the presence or absence of a given trait as such, we do not despair when we discover that a child has inherited a tendency to asthma or hay fever. Instead, we try to find out to which particular substance in the environment he is sensitive and then to create an environment in which that substance is rare or absent.

It is true that for many heredities no environments have been found as yet which will change the response appreciably. The heredity which determines our eye color, blood group type, or fingerprint type seems to produce the same traits in all known environments. The skin color, stature and weight are quite certainly hereditary, but they are also sensitive to environment. Psychic characters, such as criminality, are so sensitive to environment that the very fact that heredity has anything

at all to do with them was long in dispute. In which
class a given trait belongs depends, however, on how
much we know about the trait in question, as the example of diabetes and insulin shows.

On the whole, modern biology has strengthened the
hands of those who try to improve the minds and bodies
of men by improving the conditions in which they live.
The normal mental and emotional "Natures" are very
responsive to "Nurtures" of education and social influences. The "personality" is influenced by education,
training, opportunities, cultural contacts and similar
factors. It is acquired by us through our experience.

Biological and Cultural Determinants of Human Personality

Our intellect, our emotions, and our behavior are so
obviously influenced by education and by living conditions that some writers have doubted or even denied
outright that biological heredity has any influence whatever on the development of human personality. To many
people the existence of inheritable differences in psychic
traits seems incompatible with democratic ideals. It is
true that those who wish to withhold certain rights and
opportunities from some groups of their fellow men have
very often sought to justify their attitudes by an alleged
biological inferiority of those whom they would like to
keep in a state of submission. But we should remember
that the democratic assertion of the equality of rights is
important precisely because it helps diverse personalities
to live together and to participate in a common civilization. Anyway, the problem of the role of heredity in the
formation of human personality should be solved in accordance with ascertainable facts and regardless of our
likes and dislikes.

There is no doubt that certain abnormal conditions
of the mind and the nervous system represent the reaction
of abnormal heredity. Some of the mental diseases tend
to "run in families," and some forms of idiocy depend

on a specific inheritance. Imbeciles of one particular type have a gross disturbance of one of the normal physiological functions of the body, namely the breaking down of a chemical substance known as phenyl-pyruvic acid. This substance is present in normal people also, but a normal body uses it up, while such imbeciles excrete it in the urine. This form of mental defect is hereditary, and the lack of development of mind is somehow related to the abnormal physiological reaction just mentioned. Of course, it must not be supposed that all abnormal mental states are due to abnormal heredity. Many minds get into twilight because of alcoholism, age, infectious diseases, injuries, or other environmental bad luck. We do not know yet whether particular kinds of minds are more resistant to bad luck than others, but in view of what we know of physical characteristics it would not surprise us if this were so.

It is also certain that human behavior and states of mind are greatly influenced by physical characters which are clearly hereditary. In the victims of haemophilia or bleeder's disease the blood fails to clot at wounds, and persons with haemophilia may, and often do, bleed to death after a slight scratch. Haemophilia is hereditary; in fact, it was one of the first diseases to have its exact method of heredity worked out. One would certainly class haemophilia as a "physical" character; but consider for a moment the behavior of a boy who has haemophilia and knows it. He cannot take part in the usual sports and games for fear of a slight injury that might bring on an attack of bleeding. He may be timid, difficult, and shy where his brother is confident and aggressive. In consequence of this he may be uncertain in his action and his whole personality may be set by his disease.

Not only diseases but "normal" physical traits as well influence personality and behavior. Compare a tall and well built youth with facial features which conform to the prevalent notions of beauty with, say, an excessively fat lad with unattractive facial features. Other things being equal, the former is more likely to be popular with his companions of either sex than the latter. Now, the importance of such things as "popularity" in the formation of one's manners, habits, and even one's world outlook is considerable. On the other hand, heredity is doubtless an important factor in the determination of the body build and the facial features (which is not to deny the importance of the environment in the development of these traits as well!).

A Negro or even a "white" person with an unusually swarthy skin will probably be quite self-conscious in the company of whites if he knows or suspects that the latter are imbued with the "white superiority" prejudice. This behavior is directly related to the physical trait, namely, the skin color. The fact that in a different environment, in a society having different traditions and customs, this behavior would not appear does not make it any less hereditary in the biological sense. You must beware not to fall into the crude mistake of supposing that a trait which is modified by the environment is not hereditary, and that a hereditary trait can not be modified by the environment. Heredity determines reactions and responses in and to particular environments. Now, human personality always functions within the framework of a certain social and cultural setting, and it can not be understood apart from this framework. This simple truth was discovered and expressed more than two thousand years ago by Aristotle in his famous dictum "Man is a political animal." You can not understand man without taking both his political (social) and his animal natures into account.

Transmission of Culture

Animals and plants have only biological heredity, but man has created a highly important set of influences which can be called his cultural inheritance. By culture is meant first of all our language, which is the framework in which we are forced to fit our communication with other humans and even our own intimate thoughts. Furthermore, here belong the patterns of behavior, of reasoning, and of feelings which we are taught from infancy on, and which we take so completely for granted that we notice the very existence of these patterns only when we come into contact with people who have inherited different patterns. For example, nudism is shocking to many of us, but to other people the wearing of clothes seems a perversity. Some people eat insects but feel nauseated at the very thought of eating pork. Finally, we have inherited from our ancestors a great body of scientific and technical knowledge, treasuries of literature, poetry and music, and a system of religion and ethics. Not even completely illiterate people can escape being profoundly influenced by culture. Culture constantly, though slowly, changes, grows or deteriorates, develops or breaks up. These changes are compounded of important acquisitions contributed by eminent individuals, as well as of collective acquisitions of the masses.

Culture, in contrast to biological heredity, is not transmitted through chromosomes and sex cells. We learn to speak the language or languages which are spoken by those around us, regardless of whether they are our parents or biologically unrelated persons. Then we begin to learn from books, often written by persons whom we never saw or who died long before we were born. The transmission of cultural heredity is so efficient that peoples are able freely to acquire any one of the variety of cultures which exist in the world. Instances are numerous where children of European ancestry were adopted into Chinese or Japanese homes and grew up to be culturally Chinese or Japanese even though they preserved their "white" physical traits. Americans have special opportunities to observe that American-born children of some of the immigrants from foreign countries develop mentally like other American children, and sometimes come to resemble in outlook and behavior native Americans more than their own parents. These children have not inherited the traits produced in their parents and more remote ancestors by exposure for centuries to certain non-American cultural or material influences.

It is important to remember that such cultural acquisitions even when acting over long periods of time do not become biologically inherited. This question is part of a larger one, the so-called "inheritance of acquired characters," which is discussed later in this book. At this juncture we need only point out that no good experimental evidence exists that this is the source of the changes which occur in the hereditary constitution. The evident hereditary variety in all animal and plant species arose in other ways, as described in Chapter 3. We can take it that "acquired characters" are not inherited.

Making new discoveries in science is an exciting business, so exciting in fact that scientists have often succumbed to the temptation to make their discoveries explain everything, instead of only some things. Certain biologists have contended that human personalities and even cultures are to all intents and purposes determined by biological heredity, environment being of little consequence. Certain cultural anthropologists, whose business it is to study and compare different cultures, answered by claiming that man is entirely a creature of his culture, and that his biological heredity stops at the surface of his skin. Thus we have heard in recent years that the Japanese character is set by the early and severe toilet training of Japanese babies; while Russians are what they are because of the swaddling of infants which was practiced in Russia (and, incidentally, in many other European countries). All that needs to be said about such theories is that they fail to take into account this well-established fact: man's personality, as well as his physical traits, results from a process of development in which both heredity and environment play important parts.

Conclusions

Undoubtedly, to begin life with a normal, healthy mind, a good set of sense organs, and a sound nervous system is to have the stage set for good mental achievement. The direction, the intensity, and the particular type of achievement will often depend upon luck, teachers, books, examples for emulation, and the like, encountered when one is young. Everything we have learned about heredity leads us to think of it not as a blind, absolute, and inexorable force, but rather as the setting, the particular form of responsiveness with which we meet life. It is true we cannot change our heredity, nor for that matter can we change the essential operations of the chemical and physical world in which we live. Yet the determinate character of the physical world proved, when we started to learn about it, to provide opportunities for an enormous scientific and technical development by which we actually control some parts of our environment. So, too, when we learn to know the potentialities of our inherited constitutions and how to place them in proper relation to a controlled environment, human differences may come to be viewed in a new light.

3. The Method of Heredity

WHEN PEOPLE HAVE no real understanding of some natural process they are apt to invent an imaginary explanation. This is the way in which myths orginate. The ancient Greeks did not know the reason for the succession of day and night. They pictured the sun as the young and beautiful god Apollo riding across the sky in his bright chariot drawn by seven tireless horses. Many myths are gems of poetic imagination, some have profound philosophical meaning, but others are merely unsuccessful attempts to solve the riddles of nature. Although mythology often is pleasant reading, it is dangerous to confuse mythological and scientific explanations and to act on the basis of such mistaken ideas.

The fact that children resemble their parents is so striking and so generally recognized that it had to be fitted into the general scheme of human knowledge and beliefs. Blood was believed to have many magical properties such as to make seeds fertile when sprinkled with blood before planting, to transmit the bravery, wisdom or other qualities of the person whose blood might be drunk by an enemy, to purify the soul of one anointed with blood. Whether it was as an extension of such properties that blood was made responsible for the transmission of heredity we do not know; but a myth arose according to which the qualities of the parents are passed on to the child through the blood.

Heredity Through Blood?

Blood does of course perform important functions, but the transmission of heredity is not one of them. For some two centuries it has been known that the child arises not from the blood but from the union of two tiny cells from the parents—a single egg cell from the mother with one sperm cell from the father. But even today the old myth persists and some people speak as if blood were the carrier of heredity. In many languages it is common to hear such expressions as: "he is of my blood," "blood will tell," "half-blood," "mixed bloods," "new blood." If this usage expressed merely the lack of precision characteristic of everyday speech, little harm would result. But the situation is more serious than that, for so long as people continue to think of heredity as transmitted by blood, they will inevitably misunderstand not only the essential nature of heredity but also all of the problems, social as well as biological, in which heredity plays a part.

Heredity is what causes children to resemble their parents and other ancestors more or less closely. The resemblance is never exact and the parents are never exactly alike. One parent may be blond and the other brunet, one may be tall and the other short. It is clearly a part of the problem of heredity to discover how these differences are reflected in the children. If you compare many children with their parents, you will find that in most of their characteristics the children are intermediate between the parents. This is particularly evident when the parents differ widely, as in marriages between Negroes and whites in which the children (mulattoes) are about midway between the parents in skin color. Such observations tell us that the father and mother have about equal influence in shaping the characteristics of the child. This condition could of course occur by a mixing of parental "bloods" in the child, which might then be expected to be a blend of parental characters. But the blood theory strikes a serious snag when you find, as often occurs, that a child has some characteristics which neither parent had but which came from one of the grandparents or more remote ancestors. For example, some blue-eyed children are born in families in which both parents are brown- or black-eyed but in which other ancestors or relatives had blue eyes. In such cases we say that the blue-eyed trait has "skipped a generation." But how can "blood" skip a generation; and how can "brown-eyed blood" make children blue-eyed?

Another common fact which flatly contradicts the blood theory is that brothers and sisters, though showing a certain family resemblance, are clearly different from one another. One may be brown-eyed and another blue-eyed; one may have normal vision and another be color-blind; it is well known that brothers may belong to different blood groups so that one may not be able to give blood for transfusion to the other. Such facts clearly mean that each child (with the exception of identical twins) receives from its parents a unique heredity, different in some way or ways from the heredity passed on by the same parents to other children of the same family. How could the same parent transmit different bloods to each of his children? Now that we know the actual means by which we inherit from our parents, it seems strange that scientists should ever have taken stock in the blood theory; but as great a scientist as Darwin did and so did many others of his era and before. Great discoveries often seem simple after they have been made and the ideas they displace then seem absurd by contrast; but until the great mind, the proper circumstances and perhaps the lucky idea come together, even good scientists are apt to accept half-truths or even wrong ideas like the blood theory.

Mendel's Discovery

The discovery of the method of heredity is one of the most dramatic stories in the history of science. It occurred in an unlikely place, not in a research laboratory or a great university, but in a monastery garden in a town in Moravia which later became a part of Czechoslovakia. There a monk named Gregor Mendel worked quietly and methodically from 1857 to 1865 crossing different varieties of the garden pea and studying the differences through several generations. In 1865 he read an account of his experiments to the society of naturalists in the town of Brno (Brünn), and this was published in the journal of the society in 1866. This journal did not have a wide circulation although it was sent to a number of libraries in several countries. If any scientists read it, they paid no attention to it, for this article, which contained the gist of the modern theory of heredity, lay unnoticed until 1900. Then, 16 years after Mendel's death, three other European scientists independently made a similar discovery, unearthed Mendel's forgotten account, and it suddenly became known throughout the world. That was the origin of the science of genetics, which, from that sudden beginning in 1900, has progressed with great speed.

The simple rules or "laws" of heredity, of which the fundamental ones were discovered by Mendel, are universal in their application to all forms of life. The fact that they were discovered through experimentation on the humble vegetable, the garden pea, was due to Mendel's deliberate choice of this plant as offering special advantages for the objective he had in mind. For he knew that to solve what for centuries had been the "riddle of heredity," he must study the descendants of parents which differed in clear and unmistakable characters and must observe and count large numbers of descendants. Moreover, he had to know the exact parentage of every individual and this meant that all matings had to be made deliberately by the experimenter. Nothing could be left to accident.

Now human marriages can not be made at the command of an experimenter, at least in our kind of society; nor will men and women choose their mates because one party has blue eyes and straight hair, is taste-blind and of blood group AB, while the other has brown eyes, curly hair, is a "taster" and of blood group O. People marry for reasons other than these; and controlled experiment on heredity cannot be used as a method of study on human beings. Large domestic animals, cattle, horses, or sheep are also unfavorable because of low fertility, slow breeding, and great expense of raising large numbers. The need to observe thousands of individuals of known parentage, sometimes through dozens of generations, has led students of heredity since Mendel's time to choose for experiments the rapidly breeding vinegar fly (Drosophila), Indian corn, mice and rats, wheat, snapdragons, poultry, tobacco plants, and more recently, molds and other microorganisms. Enough has been learned about the heredity of particular traits in hundreds of other kinds of organisms to make it clear that Mendel's principles apply to all.

Mendel's Law

The essence of Mendel's discovery lay in his identification of the units of heredity. These entities, the genes, were the first living units to be discovered which are comparable to the atoms or molecules upon which our understanding of the non-living world has been based. The discovery of them has had a fructifying effect upon the whole of biology comparable to the effect of the atomic theory upon the physical sciences.

How can one apprehend such living units, which cannot be seen? In particular, how can one prove them to be discrete durable particles, endowed with the kind of individuality which molecules have? Mendel first recognized genes from the manner in which specific visible characters of plants, such, for example, as flower color, reappeared in their offspring. His method was so simple that it can be repeated by anyone who can observe the results of controlled matings in any kind of animal or plant. When a plant of a pure purple-flowered variety of pea is crossed with a white-flowered plant, the seeds so produced always yield only purple-flowered plants. When these purple-flowered plants are allowed to produce their progeny these are found to consist of *two* kinds of plants with respect to flower color: about 3/4 of them have purple flowers, and 1/4 have white flowers. When seed from these plants, the grandchildren of the original purple-flowered and white-flowered plants, was planted, it was found that although the grandchildren comprised two visibly different types, they consisted of *three* different types in respect to their ability to transmit hereditary differences in flower color. Of all of the grandchildren, 1/4 were like the purple grandparents, transmitting purple to all their offspring; 1/2 were like the purple parents, transmitting purple to some of their offspring, white to others, while 1/4 were like the white grandparents, transmitting white only to all their offspring. Actually, in one of Mendel's experiments the grandchildren consisted of 705 purple- to 224 white-flowered plants (about 3:1); while of 100 of these purples tested 36 had only purple offspring, 64 had both purple and white, i. e., about 1:2. Thus, the whole generation consisted of about 1/4 pure purple, 1/2 hybrid purple, 1/4 white. Since white is not expressed in the hybrid, Mendel called it *recessive* in contrast to the *dominant* purple which is expressed in the hybrid.

The regularity with which this ratio appeared in all of Mendel's experiments and in those of others who repeated his experiments on other kinds of plants and on animals, made it certain that some very regular and definite event determined the color of the children, whether they should be purple or white. It was very much as though one made many tosses of a pair of coins each of which had a purple side and a white side (or rather a head and tail). Anyone who has tried such an experiment knows that in about 1/4 of the tosses both coins land head side up, in 1/2 of the tosses one is head and one tail, while in the remaining 1/4 both are tails. Mendel saw that the fundamental similarity between the coins and the plants must be that purple or white flower color must depend on the same kind of event that determines the fall of a coin. It must be something that can happen in only one of two different ways.

The essence of the theory he proposed was that traits like flower color are transmitted by means of units in the sex cells. One of these units can be purple *or* white, *never* a mixture. From a pure purple parent only purple units are transmitted; from a white one only white units, but a *hybrid,* that is, a plant whose parents were of different colors, such as purple and white, transmits two kinds of units, purple ones and white ones in equal numbers. When these two kinds of eggs in large numbers are fertilized by the two kinds of pollen, there result combinations of purple with purple, purple with white, white with purple and white with white. The first three types develop into purple plants, the last into white plants; hence the ratio $\frac{1}{4}$ like one grandparent (pure purple), $\frac{1}{2}$ like the parents (hybrid purple), $\frac{1}{4}$ like the other grandparent (pure white).

Often this ratio of $\frac{1}{4}:\frac{1}{2}:\frac{1}{4}$, which is the fundamental one in all heredity, is directly observable. Thus, matings of Blue Andalusian fowls regularly produce offspring of which $\frac{1}{4}$ are black, $\frac{1}{2}$ are blue, and $\frac{1}{4}$ are white. In this case it can be inferred that blue is the impure or hybrid form which transmits both colors. This is verified by mating black birds with white ones. Only blues result. Mendel's assumptions about the units of heredity can be simply illustrated in this case by supposing that of the sperm of blue birds half will transmit black (B) and half white (b) and similarly for the eggs.

The ways in which these would combine at random are shown below:

SPERM

		$\frac{1}{2} B$	$\frac{1}{2} b$
eggs	$\frac{1}{2} B$	$\frac{1}{4} BB$ (black)	$\frac{1}{4} Bb$ (blue)
	$\frac{1}{2} b$	$\frac{1}{4} Bb$ (blue)	$\frac{1}{4} bb$ (white)

This should lead to the production of about 25 BB (black chickens), 50 Bb (blues) and 25 bb (whites) out of each hundred, or to about $\frac{1}{4}$ black: $\frac{1}{2}$ blue: $\frac{1}{4}$ white, which is just what the poultry breeders (and the biologists) found. This is exactly what Mendel discovered in every cross that he made between his different races of peas. Always, the mating between two hybrids (or of a hybrid mating with itself by self-fertilization) produced offspring of which about 1/4 were like one grandparental type, 1/2 were like the hybrid parents and 1/4 were like the other grandparental type. This is known as the "Mendelian segregation ratio" of 1:2:1, and Mendel said that it proved his theory that each of the sex cells of a hybrid could transmit one and only one of the contrasted parental characters, and that half of the sex cells must transmit one of the characters, and half must transmit the alternative one. This very assumption of alternative conditions of one unit, which the ratios required, was in fact the proof of the existence of the units themselves, and this was the revolutionary idea introduced by Mendel.

Mendel found that this theory held true for every pair of characters which he studied in the pea plant; and it has been confirmed by experiments with hundreds of other kinds of animals and plants. In all cases, it has been shown that the genes contributed to the hybrids by the parents do not mix but are segregated into the different sex cells of the hybrid, so that in the progeny of hybrids a character of the parent will reappear uncontaminated by its passage through the hybrid. This law of heredity discovered by Mendel is known as the law of segregation.

Human Genes

The operation of the law of segregation in man is shown when a sharply noticeable character like albinism crops out in a family. Albino persons lack dark pigment in hair (which is pale yellow or straw colored), skin (very light) and eyes, which take their pink color from the blood vessels in the back of the eye. When large families in which parents are normally colored contain any albino children, the albinos usually constitute about a quarter of the total, and instances of albinism in the family history will also usually be found. Moreover in a few families in which both parents are albinos all the children are albinos. These facts, and others, show that albinism is recessive, and that the normal parents of albino children are hybrid (heterozygous). If we denote the unit for albinism by a, and its counterpart present in normally pigmented people as A, then we describe these parents as Aa and expect that of their children about $\frac{1}{4}$ will be AA, about $\frac{1}{2}$ Aa (or together $\frac{3}{4}$ normal) and about $\frac{1}{4}$ aa (albinos). In various ways it has been shown that this expectation is realized. If you are normally pigmented and have an albino brother or sister, you can count *your* chances of carrying an albino gene as about 2 out of 3; because $\frac{2}{3}$ of the normals in such families should be Aa; and your chances of not carrying an albino gene as 1 out of 3 because $\frac{1}{3}$ of the normals in such families should be AA. These chances are proved to be about right by studying the offspring of brothers and sisters of albinos.

In general, light eye color (blue) behaves as recessive to dark eye color (black or brown) but it isn't as easy to separate people into two sharp classes for eye color as it is for albinism. Hazel, green, gray and flecked eyes make trouble for the classifier. But with care and caution it can be shown that Mendel's law of segregation applies to human eye color, and to many other normal traits, and to very many abnormal characters and conditions.

We mentioned earlier the existence of two kinds of persons with regard to ability to taste phenyl-thio-carbamide (PTC); that is, some can and some can't taste this substance. The ability to taste PTC is inherited just like any other Mendelian character. To determine this, one must examine the offspring coming from marriages in which neither parent can taste PTC, in which one parent is a taster and the other is taste-blind, and finally in which both parents are tasters. Such an examination was performed by Blakeslee. In 10 families with a total of 22 children in which both parents were taste-blind all the children were also taste-blind. In 54 families in which both parents were tasters, 109 children were tasters and 22 taste-blind. Finally, 39 families in which one parent was a taster and the other was taste-blind had a total of 74 children, 42 tasters and 32 taste-blind. The ability to taste PTC is due to a dominant gene, which we may call T. The inability to taste PTC is due to a recessive gene, t. A taste-blind person is always pure for t (tt), since if he carried even one T he would necessarily be a taster. If both father and mother are taste-blind, all the children are also taste-blind. A taster may be either hybrid (heterozygous) $Tt,$ or pure (homozygous) TT. If both parents are tasters and at least one of them is pure, $TT,$ all the children will be tasters. The same will be true if a pure taster, $TT,$ marries a taste-blind person tt. But if both parents are hybrid tasters (Tt), we expect among their children about $3/4$ tasters and $1/4$ taste-blind. Finally, from a hybrid taster married to a taste-blind person about half of the children should be tasters and the other half taste-blind. These expectations have been realized in studies of many families.

Abnormal Genes

Many abnormal human traits are dominant over the normal condition. This doesn't mean that abnormalities are more likely to be dominant than recessive, or that dominant traits are commoner than recessive ones, but merely that dominant abnormalities attract the attention of medical men and students of heredity and are more likely to be recorded and have their heredity worked out. After all, to have a six-fingered child or a dwarf or an albino in the family is more remarkable than to have a blue-eyed or freckled or snub-nosed child. Also the inheritance of dominant characters is easy to recognize since they do not "skip a generation." Take the case of abnormally short fingers. The medical name of this trait is brachydactyly (Greek for short-fingered). In contrast to the albino case, children with such short fingers are born only in families in which at least one of the parents is short-fingered. This trait is rare enough so that short-fingered people usually marry persons with ordinary fingers and the children fall into two categories, short and ordinary, in about equal numbers, just as Mendel found in his test cross of a hybrid to a recessive. This means that virtually all short-fingered persons are hybrid (heterozygous); and for the same reason, persons with other rare dominant defects are nearly always hybrid and transmit the defect to about half of their children. Sometimes, however, the abnormal gene occurs in an isolated village or valley where people are likely to marry neighbors and relatives and then it may happen that two with the same abnormality marry. A case of this sort was recorded by two Norwegian investigators who found a family in which both father and mother had the short-fingered trait. Two children were born; one was short-fingered; the other was a cripple with no fingers or toes at all and with other bones so abnormal that it did not live very long. This was probably pure for the short-fingered character, getting an abnormal gene from both father and mother; but the handicap was so severe that such a child could probably never live to adulthood. We should therefore not expect to find any adult who is pure (homozygous) for such an abnormality.

Combinations of Genes

In these human cases we have done what Mendel did and have picked out one pair of characters for study, neglecting all the many other characters in which parents always differ. Eventually Mendel had to face the problem of following more than one difference at a time and discovering how different pairs of characters behaved in relation to each other. What would happen, for example, if his purple-flowered pea was also tall, while the white-flowered parent was also dwarf? By following two or more pairs of characters at once, Mendel discovered another law which we call the law of independent assortment. Mendel found that when double hybrids were bred together all possible combinations occurred in the offspring by pure chance. That is, in the second generation from the cross of yellow round by green wrinkled the color of the seeds was quite independent of the seed shape. Of the $\frac{3}{4}$ yellows, $\frac{3}{4}$ were round and $\frac{1}{4}$ were wrinkled, and of the $\frac{1}{4}$ of greens $\frac{3}{4}$ were round and $\frac{1}{4}$ were wrinkled; in other words, $\frac{3}{4}$ of $\frac{3}{4}$ or $\frac{9}{16}$ were yellow round, $\frac{1}{4}$ of $\frac{3}{4}$ or $\frac{3}{16}$ were yellow wrinkled; $\frac{3}{4}$ of $\frac{1}{4}$ or $\frac{3}{16}$ were green round, and $\frac{1}{4}$ of $\frac{1}{4}$ or $\frac{1}{16}$ were green wrinkled. Describing each seed in these two ways at once, Mendel counted the following actual numbers in one experiment, and compared them with ideal numbers expected from the proportions given above.

	actual numbers of seeds	proportion of total	ideal numbers
yellow round	315	$\frac{9}{16}$	313
yellow wrinkled	101	$\frac{3}{16}$	104
green round	108	$\frac{3}{16}$	104
green wrinkled	32	$\frac{1}{16}$	35
Total	556		556

The actual figures are so close to the ideal that they may be taken to represent the proportions given, and we must conclude, as Mendel did, that the characters yellow-green, and round-wrinkled are inherited in entire independence of each other.

This independence in inheritance of separate traits of plants, animals and men was an entirely new idea which Mendel was the first to recognize and to prove. It has many important and interesting consequences. For example when Mendel crossed *two* varieties of peas, one with yellow round and one with green wrinkled seeds, he obtained four varieties in the second generation. The two new ones had yellow *wrinkled* and green *round* seeds respectively. Thus new varieties can be obtained by crossing, and the number of kinds from which the farmer or gardener may choose can be greatly increased. This is of great importance in practical agriculture. Suppose that you have two varieties of a crop or vegetable plant, and that each variety possesses an advantageous trait which the other does not have. For example, one variety may yield well but may not have sufficient resistance to frost, while the other is frost resistant but produces unsatisfactory yields. It it obviously desirable to have a combination of good yield and frost resistance in the same plants. If yield and resistance are chiefly influenced by two pairs of independent genes, then according to Mendel's second law, this may often be accomplished by crossing the two varieties, and selecting in the second generation of hybrids the plants which possess the desired combination of traits. Plants in which the undesirable qualities of the initial varieties are combined will also appear among the hybrids, making a careful examination of individual plants and their progenies essential. Many of the best varieties of cultivated plants have been arrived at by combining through appropriate crosses the desirable traits which were present separately in several older varieties.

Causes of Variety

Independent inheritance greatly increases the numbers of different kinds of individuals. Mendel showed that when two races of plants differed by three independent characters, such as one with yellow round seeds and purple flowers and another with green wrinkled seeds and white flowers, the descendants of a cross between these varieties were of eight different types, i.e., each of the four combinations of yellow, round, green and wrinkled could be either purple or white, which doubled the numbers of combinations. In fact every additional pair of independent character differences which show dominance doubles the number of combinations. If in a human family we have differences such as (1) taster or taste-blind; (2) dark or light eyes; (3) short-fingered or normal; we have 8 possible combinations. As anyone can tell by looking about him, the number of human character differences is much greater than three, so the number of combinations must be very large.

The following table shows the number of types which theoretically must appear among the hybrids when the parents differ in a certain number of dominant genes:

Gene differences	Types among the progeny
1	2
2	4
3	8
4	16
5	32
...	...
10	1,024
...	...
20	1,048,576
...	...
30	1,073,741,824
...	...
n	2^n

The number of distinct types (gene combinations) grows to more than a thousand when parents differ in 10 genes, to more than a million with 20, and to more than a billion with 30 gene differences. With 31 gene differences it becomes about equal to the total number of humans now living in the world, which is estimated as close to 2,500 millions. With still greater numbers of gene differences the numbers of possible gene combinations become immense. With about 250 genes the number of theoretically possible gene combinations is of the same order as that of the electrons and protons in the universe as estimated by some physicists.

Such calculations may seem meaningless, because nothing can be more certain than that only an extremely small fraction of all the possible gene combinations can ever actually occur. This is true enough, but the calculations serve to bring out an important point. Suppose that an average human individual is hybrid for only ten genes; this is a very conservative estimate, and the true figure is probably greater. Now, such a hybrid produces 1,024 distinct types of sex cells, and is capable of engendering that many different types of offspring. We see then, that the chance of two brothers or sisters receiving the same hereditary endowment from their father or from their mother is small. The chance that they receive the same endowment from both parents is quite negligible, unless, of course, the brothers are identical twins. As we now know, identical twins arise from a single egg, and have the same genes.

How many genes there are in man is unknown, but it would seem reasonable to believe that man has at least as many as the vinegar-fly, Drosophila. To be sure, the number of genes is not precisely known even in that insect, which has been studied more than any other animal; but it is estimated that a Drosophila has several thousands, perhaps as many as ten thousand genes in each sex cell.

To appreciate the difficulty of counting the genes in any animal or plant, one must have a clear idea about the method through which one learns about the existence of the genes in the first place. Mendel observed the segregation of the purple and white flower colors in the offspring of a hybrid between the purple and white varieties, and concluded that the pea plant must have a gene for flower color. He was able to discover this because a gene for flower color had, in the past, assumed two different forms, one leading to development of color, the other to no color. The event which produces such a difference in gene form, and hence in its effect, is known as *mutation*. This process, as the original source of variety, will be discussed in the next chapter. Our knowledge of the genes for tasting PTC, for eye color, for albinism, and for brachydactyly in man comes from observations on the distribution of tasters and non-tasters, brown and blue eyes, albinos and non-albinos, and short and normal fingers in selected human pedigrees. But imagine that all the peas existing in the world or known to us are purple (or all white), or that PTC has never been prepared or tasted. The existence of the genes for the flower color in peas and for tasting PTC in man would not even be suspected. In other words, we find out about the existence of a gene for a given trait only if we observe individuals which differ with respect to that trait, and, strictly speaking, only if such individuals can be crossed and a Mendelian segregation in their offspring can be observed. This means that we can identify and count only those genes which have undergone mutation and now occur in two or more different alternative forms. By no means all traits in Drosophila have been observed to vary in different individuals. The appraisal of the total number of genes in that insect has been arrived at by very different indirect methods which we need not discuss here.

We have seen that hereditary differences between brothers and sisters can easily be accounted for if the parents are hybrid for several genes. Brothers, sisters, and relatives in general tend, however, to show family resemblances; the differences between non-relatives are on the whole greater than between relatives. If man has no fewer genes than a Drosophila fly, a human sex cell must carry several thousand genes. Let us assume that only about three hundred of these genes are each represented by at least two alternative conditions such as A and a, dominant and recessive. This is almost certainly an underestimate, but for the purposes of the argument we are going to make, an underestimate is preferable to an overestimate. Three hundred gene differences are capable of producing a fantastic number of combinations—more than there are electrons and protons in the Universe. Although we can not as yet make an exact count of human genes, we can be very sure that all the gene combinations which exist in all the humans living in the world constitute just a negligibly small fraction of gene combinations that could be formed.

Each Man Is Unique

We can not tell whether the innumerable missing gene combinations would make men better or worse than those which happen to exist. All we can tell is that mankind is capable of producing an almost infinitely greater collection of types than that which exists at present or existed in the past. The chance that any two human beings, now living or having lived, have identical sets of genes is practically zero, identical twins always excepted. The hereditary endowment which each of us has is strictly his own, not present in anybody else, unprecedented in the past, and almost certainly not repeatable in the future. A biologist must assert the absolute uniqueness of every human individual. This same assertion, translated into metaphysical and political terms is fundamental for both ethics and democracy.

A father and a mother transmit different sets of genes to each of their children. A human sex cell has one gene of each of the kinds which we have discussed (for eye color, taste reaction to PTC, albinism versus normal coloration, brachydactyly versus normal fingers), and, of course, one of each of the many other genes which the human species must have. We estimate that there must be several thousands of genes in the full set carried in a human sex cell. Fertilization of an egg by a sperm results in the development of the new individual. Since the baby gets one gene of each kind from each parent, it follows that it has two of each kind. If there are five thousand different genes in the egg and five thousand in the sperm cell, there will be five thousand pairs or ten thousand altogether in every cell composing the body of the individual. However, when sex cells, whether eggs or sperms, are formed in that individual there is an exact biological mechanism in the body which ensures that each egg or sperm will receive one gene of each pair. It is clear, therefore, that each parent transmits to its child always only ½, never all, the genes it has. The next child, developing from a different sex cell, will have also ½ of the genes which each parent has, but it will be, as we know, a different set of genes for every child.

Ancestral Heredity

Approximately, but only approximately, ¼ of all of the genes of a grandchild comes from each of its four grandparents. It will sometimes happen that one of the grandparents will have contributed more and another grandparent less than his equal share of the genes of a grandchild. It might even happen that a grandchild will inherit no genes at all from one of its grandparents, and ½ of its genes from another grandparent. To be sure, such an extreme case is unlikely to happen because man has, as we know, several thousand different genes. The probability of the extreme case is, therefore, very much less than that of a grand slam at bridge. But different grandchildren (who are brothers or sisters among themselves) will be likely to inherit somewhat different sets of genes from each of their grandparents. Each of the great-grandparents contributes on the average ⅛ of the genes of each of the great-grandchildren. Here again variations will occur. A great-grandparent may contribute either more (up to ½) or less than ⅛ (down to none). What proportion of the genes of a grandparent or a remoter ancestor will survive in his descendants will depend entirely on chance and in no way on the ancestor's bodily strength or weakness, virtues or sins.

According to the refuted "blood" theory of heredity, we inherit ½ of our hereditary endowment from each parent, ¼ from each grandparent, ⅛ from each great-grandparent, etc. This idea has taken such firm root, not only in the popular imagination but even in biology, that even now one still hears and reads of a person having ¼, ⅛, or some other fraction of "blood" of some particular race or individual. The most cherished pride of many people is the supposed fact that some fraction of their "blood" is derived from a noble ancestor, or from a passenger on the Mayflower, or from a real or a trumped-up great man or woman. We can see how preposterous such claims are. To be sure, an individual receives on the average ¼ of his genes from each grandparent, ⅛ from each great-grandparent, etc. But this is only a statistical average, and in reality one may have either more or fewer, down to no genes at all, especially from the more remote ancestors. More important still, all the qualities of our ancestors were not necessarily due to their genes. And even if they were, then the important thing may have been a particularly lucky combination of genes. Such a combination is quite unlikely to remain intact in the heredity even for one generation, let alone for many, because the mechanism of heredity is to produce recombinations of the different genes which are so numerous that they are unlikely to repeat. Even some serious writers have failed to understand this and have deluded themselves into believing that they have "explained" the greatness of a great man by finding that some priceless "biological strain" has "persisted" in his "blood" by transmission from some particular ancestor.

Single genes are not solely responsible for single characters or body parts. Anyone who realized the complexity of any part of the body and its continual dependence on other parts could not think of any part such as an eye as due to one thing or event. One gene may make the difference between brown eye color and blue, but obviously there had to be an eye, with its retina and iris, its nerve and blood supply, its pigment and other materials, before eye color could be expressed at all. The thousands of genes which constitute a human being interact with each other in such ways that each gene affects many parts and processes although one of these effects may be more apparent or showy than the others as in the case of eye color.

Negro-White Intermarriage

A clear example of the influence of many different genes on what seem to be simple attributes or characters is to be seen wherever colored and white races have intermarried. Skin color in the offspring of marriages between Negroes and whites is of an intermediate shade. The mulatto is neither black nor white. Considering skin color only, the children of marriages between mulattoes are very variable from light through intermediate shades to black. Attempts to analyze the inheritance of skin color in Mendelian terms have not been very successful because "white" and "Negro" each include a number of different skin colors, and many other factors such as tanning and bleaching also affect skin color. But there is little doubt that at least two and probably several gene differences are concerned.

The number of gene differences between the races entering the cross is important because it determines how often individuals resembling the parent races will appear in the second and later generations after a cross. We have seen that, if Negroes and whites differ in only two genes for skin color, only one child in sixteen will have a black skin, and one in sixteen will have a white skin, in the offspring of mulatto marriages. With three genes showing no dominance, the chance of a white-skinned child would drop to one in sixty-four, with four genes to one in 256, with n genes to one in 4^n. In marriages of mulattoes with whites, the chances of birth of a child with a white skin are much higher: 1 in 4 with two genes, 1 in 8 with three, 1 in 2^n with n genes.

One of the greatest absurdities of the so-called race problem in the United States is that anyone who admits having some African ancestry is classed as a Negro regardless of his or her appearance. A "Negro" is, then, a member of a social and economic group rather than of a purely biological one. Some of the children born to such "Negroes" are indistinguishable from, and "pass" among, the whites in order to avoid anti-Negro discrimination. To estimate how frequently "passing" children will be born to parents of mixed European-African ancestry, we must take into account several characters. Most of the natives of Europe differ from a majority of the inhabitants of tropical Africa in skin color, as well as in hair form, thickness of lips, and other external traits.

The inheritance of these differences has, unfortunately, not been worked out in detail, but it is known that most of them are about as complex as the skin color is. Furthermore, the genes which influence these traits seem to be inherited independently.

The total number of genes in which Negroes differ from whites is not known, and, as will be shown below, such a number would not tell us much anyway. However, it is possible to say that if only the few differences named above are taken into account, a dozen genes would be a very conservative estimate. If so, the frequency of individuals indistinguishable from whites among the offspring of first-generation mulattoes would be quite negligible (one in 4^{12}, or in 16,777,216 children!). Even among the children of the marriages in which one of the parents is white and the other a first generation mulatto, all "white" genes will appear in only one among 2^{12}, or 4,096 children. These figures must, however, be taken with a grain of salt if we want to apply them to practical problems of the United States population. What they really show is the probability of birth of a "passing" child if, first, all whites uniformly differ from all Negroes in twelve genes, and if, second, an individual carrying any one of these genes is clearly distinguishable from any individual of exclusively white ancestry. Neither of these two stipulations is fulfilled in practice. We know that in the white population of the United States, as well as in the population of any European country, there are individuals with pale and with swarthy skin, with straight, wavy, and curly hair, with thin, average, and thick lips, etc. Some of the descendants of the Negro-white marriages resemble occasional types encountered amongst white peoples.

The stories of births of mulatto children to white parents are unfounded. As we know, the pigmentation of the human skin depends on the presence of genes which are neither dominant nor recessive; the amount of the pigment formed in the skin of a child depends on the number of these pigment-producing genes which an individual carries, and on his environment. It stands to reason then that an individual with a white skin can not possibly harbor these genes in a latent condition, regardless of whether or not he has some remote Negro ancestry. We can now answer the question frequently put to students of heredity. Suppose that a person with "white" skin, but having remote Negro ancestry, marries a white spouse. Can such a couple ever produce a black child? The answer is clearly in the negative. The darkest skin color in a child from such a marriage can hardly be much darker than that of the spouse having the Negro ancestry. The occurrence of children in mulatto families who are darker, or lighter, than either parent in no way contradicts this. When *both* parents carry a gene, or genes, for dark, or for light skin color, some of their children may inherit the sum of the genes for the dark pigmentation, or for the light pigmentation, which their parents had. This does not happen in families in which the genes for the dark pigment are brought in by only one of the parents.

Summary

IN THIS CHAPTER we have tried to let the reader look behind the external features of animals, plants and men and get a glimpse of the exact mechanism which governs heredity. Heredity consists not of blood but of genes which come in packages just as discrete and real as atoms or molecules. We receive them from our parents and pass them on to our children according to the simple regular laws which Mendel discovered. The existence of many kinds of genes and the operation of the laws by which they are dealt out to the children account for the almost infinite variety of persons in the world. But the importance of genes is not limited to explaining differences between individuals. Groups of persons look alike because they have some of their genes in common. Groups which differ biologically tend to differ in some of their genes. Most genes stand for useful qualities of good physique, good health and a good mind; but some stand for bad qualities and diseases.

The variety which is characteristic of all human groups is due to gene mutation and to recombination, as these processes have occurred in the long history of human evolution, and as they are occurring today. The outcome of such processes is discussed in the next chapter.

4. Man as a Product of Evolution

UNDERSTANDING MAN and his place in the universe is perhaps the central problem of all science. The year 1859 is, then, a red-letter date in the history of thought, for in that year Charles Darwin published his theory of evolution, which has deeply affected not only biology but the whole world outlook of modern man. Darwin showed that the human species, as well as the enormous variety of animals and plants that we find about us, are the outcome of a long and gradual process of development which has been taking place during the two billion years of the earth's history. This evolutionary process is still going on, and will in all probability continue in the future. The causes of past evolution are still in operation, and they can, therefore, be studied, understood, and, we may hope, eventually subjected to some measure of control by man.

To believe that man arose from ancestors who were not men seemed blasphemy to many of Darwin's contemporaries. Even now occasional misguided persons try to fight the view that man is a part of nature. Most people, however, greeted the scientific proof of this view as a great liberation from spiritual bondage, and saw in it the promise of a better future. The theory of evolution is basically optimistic, for it holds that nature is subject to change and that man's fate has not been finally decided. The process of Creation which Michelangelo depicted on the ceiling of the Sistine Chapel in Rome is a symbolic representation not only of a remote past but of present and future events as well. A better world and better men may yet emerge.

Natural Selection

Darwin supposed that evolution is a consequence of the process by which organisms become adapted to different environments. This adaptation is brought about by a mechanism which he called natural selection. Every species of animals and plants contains some individuals which, by their heredity, are better fitted than their fellows to survive and to leave a large progeny. Some tigers are more expert than others at catching prey, and some prey are more expert than others at escaping from tigers. The tigers that catch more prey, and the prey that escape most often, will live longer and have more offspring than those which go hungry or get eaten up. As time goes on, tigers will become more and more expert catchers and their prey more and more expert escapers. The survival and reproduction of the relatively better adapted individuals, will, if their differences be due to their heredity, bring about progressively greater fitness of each species to its particular way of life.

The changes which this theory has undergone in the nearly one hundred years since its publication can not be discussed here. It is enough to repeat the general verdict of modern biologists that the theory was all right as far as it went. Experimental studies of heredity since 1900 have caused some very important additions and alterations to be made. The most important is the recognition that heredity is transmitted not through some continuous substance like blood but through discrete entities, the genes. The processes of gene segregation and recombination, which are inevitable accompaniments of sexual reproduction, continually generate an immense variety of hereditary constitutions. These different heredities are then tested by natural selection, and those which fit their possessors for life in a particular environment are perpetuated in the descendants and eventually become established as the "normal" condition of that race or species. The less fit combinations of genes gradually disappear through failure to be perpetuated at the same rate as the more fit. The supply of new variants is kept up by the process of mutation, which, as is set forth below, occasionally changes old genes into new ones. The number of new combinations of genes which thereby become possible is practically unlimited, and there is accordingly no limit to evolutionary achievement.

"Social Darwinism"

In science, as in other fields of human thought, progress is often uneven or discontinuous. Brilliant achievements may be followed by wrong moves into blind alleys. After Darwin, while biologists were so preoccupied with studies on evolution that they did not look far beyond the immediate confines of their science, there grew up a strange mixture of oversimplified biology and political notions which is sometimes referred to as "social Darwinism." To many people this mixture is Darwinism; hence the groundless accusations that Darwin invented a theory of hatred and inhumanity.

Some of Darwin's followers took upon themselves the popularization and propaganda for the theory of evolution not only among biologists but also among laymen. Quite inadvertently they made some subtle changes in emphasis which had unforeseen repercussions. Thus, Herbert Spencer coined the expression "survival of the fittest" to describe the essential principle of Darwin's theory which would be expressed better without the superlative. Yet, this expression caught the imagination of biologists and non-biologists alike. There is something thrilling as well as forbidding in the image of "nature red in tooth and claw" commanding all its creatures to wage everlasting war of everybody against everybody else according to the motto "eat or be eaten." And this bloody mess was supposed to result not in universal debacle, but, miraculously, in "progress" itself! As one modern author puts it, "it was a cheerful thought that no good thing was ever lost and no lost thing was any longer any good."

Applications to human problems of the real as well as of the misconstrued Darwinism were bound to come. Francis Galton, the founder of the eugenics movement, was a relative and a follower of Darwin. Many authors further removed from scientific biology than Galton reasoned simply that if strife and bloodshed engender improvements in nature they would do so in human society as well. This seemed to be nothing else but application to man of inexorable "laws of nature." So, the Superman created by the German philosopher Nietzsche became promptly identified with the surviving fittest. Since the nineteenth and the early twentieth centuries were the period when powerful nations were building their colonial empires, it was comforting to think that when savages armed with a sling or with bow and arrow were killed or enslaved by cannon and machine gun we were simply witnessing biologically inferior stocks being replaced by biologically superior ones. The same "law of nature" works to justify wars between the "superior" nations. Hitler was by no means original when he said "mankind has grown in eternal wars, it will decay in eternal peace." To be sure, the physically more fit individuals are the ones most likely to be killed off in modern warfare, but this can be compensated by systematic atrocities against the civilians!

The idea that the stronger is biologically and "scientifically" justified in destroying the weaker has as much application to the struggles within as between nations. One simply says that the existing pyramid of wealth and power is the outcome of valuable heredity concentrating at the top and the biologically inferior classes settling further and further down. The more liberal trend among the "social Darwinists" admits that enough good genes are left in the "lower classes" to give rise to occasional valuable individuals who should be permitted to climb the social ladder. The conservatives are satisfied that the existing inequalities place everybody where he biologically belongs. Both the liberals and the conservatives are sure that abrogation of social inequalities would result in biological disaster, and view with alarm the biologically subversive trends toward such things as progressive taxation, free education, social security, and other "coddling" of the supposed carriers of inferior genes. Only few go to the length of urging that charity be withheld from the poor and medical help from those afflicted with hereditary diseases. But many argue that these things are permissible only if supplemented by measures, such as sterilization, which would remedy the biological harm done by our refusal to follow the law of the jungle.

To some people humanitarian ideas are so dear that they are prepared to argue that the weak should be helped rather than exterminated, even if posterity were to be biologically harmed by such a course. To do otherwise would be ruinous to those now living and to posterity as well. However, before we admit the existence of any such dilemma, we ought to make sure that there actually is a law of nature which demands strife as the price of biological survival.

Who Is the Fittest?

Not even among the animals and plants of the jungle is relentless struggle and bloodshed a necessary price of evolutionary survival and progress. Biologists know that mutual toleration and cooperation are just as ubiquitous in nature as exploitation and predation. Surely, the growing trees in a forest compete with each other for light and space. And yet, the trees and other forest inhabitants form a biological community of interdependent members, some of which at least can not exist without the others. We know that there exist a multitude of germs and parasites which incapacitate or kill their animal or human hosts. But there exist also less publicized organisms, for example those living in the intestines of every human being, which not only cause no appreciable harm but may even be useful by manufacturing some of the vitamins needed by the human body. Some animals and plants have become so completely dependent upon such associated organisms that they die when the association is broken. This condition of mutual aid between members of different species is so widespread in both animal and plant kingdoms that a special word, *symbiosis,* living together, has been coined for it.

It is a plausible though not fully confirmed hypothesis that parasites which seriously incapacitate or kill their hosts have only recently (on an evolutionary time scale) become parasitic on that species. Consider that not only the welfare but the very existence of parasites depends upon the availability of hosts to support them. When a parasite causes a disease which is fatal to the host, the parasite usually kills itself together with its carrier. Conversely, when two or more organisms are mutually useful, the fitness and the chances of survival are improved for each of them. Natural selection tends, therefore, to promote cooperation, and to minimize competition among organisms. In the process of evolution host and parasite species become mutually adjusted and establish first a toleration, then cooperation, and finally interdependence.

Mankind is a biological species and a part of nature. But man is also a unique being, the possessor and the creator of a social organization and of culture. He is the "political animal." No end of misconceptions and of errors are due to failures to grasp the significance of this duality of man. It is bad biology as well as dangerous deceit to say that man is "nothing but an ape with a few extra tricks." These extra tricks make him man, not ape. And it is absurd to say that considering man a biological species "degrades him to the level of beasts" —an opinion shared by some religious cranks and by the Communist Party of Russia! Man is a product of biological evolution. But man's evolution is profoundly influenced by his humanness and his culture. The folly of attempts often made by biologists to understand human biological evolution without reference to his culture is only matched by the disregard of biology in the writings of some psychologists and sociologists.

The human species has evolved an adaptive mechanism which in its power and effectiveness has no precedent in all the billion years of living evolution. This mechanism is the human brain. Animals and plants become adapted to their environments through changes in their bodily structures and functions. Man attains mastery of his environments chiefly through discovery and invention. It is thanks to the activities of his brain, and to the preservation and sharing of these activities by which they are magnified and accumulated—in short, to his cultural inheritance, that he has been able to spread all over the varied world. To this and not to his ability to make war is due his "conquest" of the earth. As a biological species man has proved to be a remarkably fit product of evolution by natural selection. He has far outstripped many animal species which far exceed him in bodily strength or prowess.

What, then, are the properties which make man biologically fit? The answer is clear: in man, biological fitness largely coincides with his fitness to live in the society of which he is a member. The demands made by different societies are variable. Some require submission of the individual, others set a higher value on personal independence and initiative; some favor greed, while others magnify generosity; in some, selfishness is encouraged, in others self-sacrifice. But all societies, primitive as well as advanced, by their existence and survival place a premium on brain power, on the ability which permits the individual to learn from experience and to modify his behavior accordingly.

The assertion frequently made by persons superficially acquainted with biology that natural selection has ceased to operate on the human level cannot survive critical examination. It is based on the assumption that "natural selection" must always involve a direct struggle of everyone against everybody and must leave in its train heaps of corpses as the price of progress. We have seen, however, that there is no basis for such an assumption, even for organisms below man in the evolutionary scale.

Bad Genes

The qualities which natural selection favors or discriminates against depend upon the environment in which the animal or plant lives. What is "bad" for the individual in one place, for example a tropical forest or a desert, may be "good" in another, such as the Arctic seas. The qualities favored in man are in part, of course, the animal qualities which had survival value in his ancestors, and those anatomical and physiological adaptations, such as resistance to specific diseases, which permit him to survive in a variety of habitats. There are other qualities, however, which, living as he does in human environments, are preeminently human qualities, and first and foremost amongst these are qualities of brain and sense organs. A powerful brain and a great spirit may sometimes reside in a weak body, and we all know of great men who were invalids for much of their lives. To say this is not to deny the importance of bodily strength and health. The ideal is certainly a sound brain in a sound body; *mens sana in corpore sano* has been the motto of ancient as well as many modern societies.

It is perfectly evident that this ideal is far from being reached at the present stage of human evolution. Quite apart from the crippling and stultifying effects of bad environment and inadequate nutrition, which are the lot of a large proportion of the world's population, there are particular genes and combinations of genes which are bad in nearly all human environments. Thus, there is one form of a gene which when received by a child from both parents renders him a deaf mute. The world of sound does not begin to exist for an infant with this condition, and the child does not start to speak unless given a special training, because it never hears anyone else speak. Two normal parents may have a deaf mute child, because both of them, without being aware of the fact, carry a recessive gene for deafness.

Many people are blind, because they inherited particular genes. An appreciable proportion of the many blind persons in the United States are victims of defective genes. Not all of these have the same gene for blindness. Indeed, over a hundred different hereditary eye diseases are known, some dominant, others recessive.

Probably all organs of the body are subject to defects brought about by specific genes. There is a dominant gene which makes the bones brittle, so that slight jolts produce fractures. There is another which reduces arms and legs to stumps, and many other genes producing different minor malformations, while still others express themselves in defects in heart, lungs, blood, and in many bodily functions.

Perhaps the most tragic of all human woes are mental defects and diseases, and some of these are undoubtedly inherited. There is one gene, a recessive, which where received from both parents, gives rise to a form of idiocy accompanied by blindness. A baby seems normal at birth, but a loss of vision and mental deterioration occurs at the age of about five to six months. Complete blindness and idiocy are soon reached, and death ensues usually during the second year of life. A rather similar condition, but due to a different recessive gene, is known as juvenile amaurotic idiocy. Here the mental decline sets in at about six years of age, and death occurs at about the age of adolescence. Amaurotic idiocy is, fortunately, a rare condition. In Sweden about one out of every 40,000 babies born becomes an amaurotic idiot. Another form of idiocy, due to a single recessive gene, results from the failure of one of the biochemical processes of the body by which proteins are broken down. The mental arrest in this case sets in later than in the preceding cases and is not so severe, although these so-called phenylpyruvic imbeciles are never self-supporting and never have children.

Although the frequency of any gene with consequences as disastrous as those above is kept down by natural

selection, through the early death of individuals showing the effects of the gene, there are unfortunately very
many such genes which express themselves in mental
deficiency so that the aggregate effect is considerable.

Genes responsible for mental illnesses which manifest
themselves after the age of reproduction has been
reached would not be held in check by early death.
Unfortunately little is known about the mode of inheritance of the different mental disorders, and it is generally recognized that many of the genes responsible may
express themselves only under particular conditions of
environment, disease, and stress. Some authorities estimate that as many as five per cent of the American population suffer from mental disease at some time during
their lives. It is certain that not all mental disease or
mental deficiency is due to bad genes. Epilepsy, for example, is probably more often caused by injury or other
disease than by a defective gene. There are, nevertheless,
many genes which produce defects in most of the human
environments which we have thus far been able to
provide.

To be contrasted with these bad genes are those hundreds or thousands of different useful ones, most of
them helping to produce the good and useful characters
of mind and body which have enabled man to rise from
savagery and build civilized societies. It is difficult to
estimate the ratio between these and those which are
defective and lead to characters which are harmful both
to the individual and to society, but man's evolutionary
success shows that he had the necessary kinds of genes.

Some authorities believe that the possessors of defective genes are now reproducing more rapidly than the
possessors of normal genes, and thus that mankind is
headed for a biological twilight. This trend, which is the
opposite of that expected from natural selection, is said
to be due to the reversal of natural selection by human
agency. Modern civilization, better nutrition, hygienic
improvements, and especially modern medicine, save
from death and prolong the life of many weaklings and
victims of hereditary defects who would die off under

"natural" conditions, meaning by "natural" the living conditions of savages or of animals. Human kindness and the desire to help the unhappy and the weak lead to the survival and propagation of defective genes. These arguments appear so plausible and the problem involved so grave that an intelligent person must give them some thought. This is doubly true, because these arguments are exploited by those who would like to withhold the benefits of modern science and technology from great masses of people under the pretext of permitting "nature" to preserve by selection the biological powers of the masses for posterity.

Genes in Mixed Populations

Where does the great variety of bad genes come from? Has the hereditary endowment of mankind really become hopelessly diseased? To consider some answers to these questions we must understand how genes change by mutation (p. 76), how particular forms of genes spread through populations, and why it is that the gene mixtures that distinguish different human populations tend to remain more or less constant from generation to generation. The last named problem was taken up independently and simultaneously by Hardy, an English mathematician, and by Weinberg, a German physician, in 1908, not long after the rediscovery of Mendel's law, and led to a great clarification of the nature of biological populations.

Now, the ideal way to study the behavior of human genes in mixed populations would be, one might think, to mix a known number of genes of one kind (actually of persons carrying that kind of gene) with a known number of genes of another kind, and to observe such a mixed population after one, two and several generations. Could one, for example, find one of those hospitable South Pacific islands inhabited by a thousand black people, and drop upon it one fine day, a thousand blond Americans? To ask such a question is to state the difficulties and limitations of this way of studying it, for even were such an experiment possible, it would defeat its ends, for if there were a preference for blonds or for brunets (as there often is), marriage would hardly be at random and this would give little scope for the genes to distribute themselves by chance. Moreover, blondness and black skin do not differ by just one pair of genes; and counting and classifying all the intermediate hues of skin color from black through khaki and café au lait to more or less white would be troublesome and unsatisfactory.

These difficulties would be got around if we could find a character which was due to just one gene difference, and if this character was not noticeable and therefore would not influence mate selection. We have already described such a character in Chapter 1. About thirty per cent of Americans are unable to taste the substance known as phenyl-thio-carbamide (PTC) while to seventy per cent this substance has an unpleasant bitter taste. There is a dominant gene T for tasting, and a recessive t for taste-blindness. Now, most people have never heard of PTC, and a man could seldom know whether a particular girl could or could not taste it, and, even though he knew, this would not influence the zeal with which he sought to marry her. Under such conditions we can be sure that marriage has been a random affair with respect to PTC.

Suppose now we drop upon an empty island a large population consisting of seventy per cent tasters and thirty per cent non-tasters. What proportion of tasters and non-tasters will there be after one, two, three or more generations? This question is virtually answered for us by the description of the American population, for each time it is examined, by different investigators, it is found to consist of about seventy per cent tasters and thirty per cent non-tasters. It is as though a mixture of just this sort had been dropped upon the United States at some past time.

To understand just how this proportion maintains itself "in equilibrium," the reader should consult the

Appendix. The important fact discussed there in detail is that no matter what may be the proportions of tasters and non-tasters in the population of an island or a country, these proportions will persist indefinitely. Of course, this is true not only for the genes T and t which are responsible for the ability or inability to taste PTC, but for any other genes as well, provided only that persons who do and who do not carry these genes live about equally long and have on the average the same number of children. Such genes found commonly in a population today will remain just as common centuries later, and rare genes will continue rare. Contrary to what the names "dominance" and "recessiveness" seem to imply, the dominant genes do not crowd out the recessive ones, nor do the recessives crowd out the dominants. The frequency of each gene tends to remain constant.

The Gene Pool

We can consider the genes of all the inhabitants of a town, country, continent, or of the whole world as belonging to great pools of genes. These pools of genes are the hereditary endowments of the populations of these towns, countries, continents, or of the world. The genes of mankind of the future will necessarily be drawn from the pool of genes of living mankind, just as our genes were drawn from the gene pool of our ancestors. The genes for tasting and not tasting PTC, for albinism and for colored hair, for normal minds, for insanity and for idiocy, good, bad, and indifferent genes, all are represented in the gene pool, each gene with a certain frequency.

As shown in the Appendix, it is easy to calculate the frequency of a gene in the gene pool of a population if we know how frequent in that population are persons who show this gene. For example, in the United States about 30 per cent of the population (which is the same as to say 0.30 of the whole) are unable to taste PTC. The frequency of a recessive gene in the gene pool is equal to the square root of the frequency in the population of persons showing the effects of that gene. Since non-tasting is recessive to tasting, the proportion of the gene t for non-tasting in the gene pool is the square root of 30 per cent, or about 5.5 per cent ($\sqrt{0.30} = .055$) of all the genes of the T-t kind. It is equally easy to find the proportion of persons in a population who will show the effects of a gene if we know the frequency of that gene in the gene pool. The frequency of persons showing the effects of a recessive gene is the square of the frequency of this gene. For example, if a recessive gene is found in $\frac{1}{10}$ of the gene pool (10 per cent, or 0.10 of the whole), about 1 per cent ($0.10^2 = 0.01$) of the population will have this gene in duplicate and will show its effects.

We can, then, predict with confidence that the present proportions of blue-eyed and brown-eyed persons in New York City will be found in New York some centuries hence, unless one or more of the following things happen.

(1) Relatively more blue-eyed (or brown-eyed) people come to New York or leave New York to live in other places.

(2) Blue-eyed (or brown-eyed) persons acquire some advantage over the other type in health, or length of life, or fertility, or some other quality which results in one class tending to have more children than the other.

(3) A means is discovered by which brown-eyed genes can be made deliberately to change into blue-eyed genes or vice versa.

New Genes by Mutation

We have now to ask a question pointed at the very root of the problem of evolution: What is the origin of the variety of genes which is found in all populations? It is not difficult to understand why, given a gene for brown eyes and its alternative for blue eyes, both forms should persist in the population if neither has an advantage over the other. But suppose that a defective gene (like that for amaurotic idiocy) is recessive to the normal condition, and that all the defectives die before they can have children. The genes present in the defectives are always lost, and their number in the population should decrease.

Unfortunately, there is no reason to believe that hereditary diseases are in process of disappearance. In fact, some figures make it look as though such diseases are becoming more frequent, but this is probably a false appearance due to improved statistics and not to worsened health. During the few decades, a century at most, for which anything like reliable statistics are available, the incidence of hereditary diseases has probably remained stable. How can this happen if some defective genes are lost in every generation? The explanation is that some genes change from normal to defective by a process known as mutation.

Mutations have been observed and studied chiefly in animals and plants. So many millions of these have now been observed under experimental control that, even though mutations are rare, thousands of them have been catalogued and studied. In man they are less easy to ascertain because to do so we must know very well the behavior of a trait in heredity. After all, children carrying a recessive gene in double dose (say, amaurotic idiots, or, for that matter, non-tasters of PTC) are quite frequently born to parents neither of which show the trait in question. As we know, this is simply Mendelian segregation. Mutation is the origin of an hereditary trait which did not exist at all in the parents of the mutant. Suddenly, among many normal offspring, a single individual is born with some unexpected trait, which is then transmitted to the offspring of that individual.

Mutations to dominant traits are detected more easily than those to recessive ones; this is because dominant genes are not in general present in the parents of the suspected mutant without being manifest in their external appearance, while recessive genes are regularly thus concealed. A colored woman born in 1853 in Louisiana from normal colored parents proved to be piebald, that is, her skin was irregularly splotched with white. She had fifteen children by a normal colored man, eight of which were also piebalds. At least five of these are known to have had in turn some piebald progeny, while no piebalds were born to their non-piebald brothers and sisters. It is fairly sure that the baby girl born in 1853 arose from a sex cell which contained a newly arisen dominant mutant gene. This gene she transmitted, as expected, to about half of her offspring. Several instances in which a dominant hereditary defect not present in the pedigree appeared suddenly in a single child born of normal parents are recorded in the medical literature. It is certain that at least some of these instances represent authentic mutations.

Precisely why mutations occur in man or in other organisms we do not know as yet. Mutations appear more frequently in the offspring of individuals treated with X rays, high temperature, and some chemicals. But mutations also occur without any treatments. For all we know, they just happen. It has, for example, been estimated that about one in every 100,000 human sex cells carries a newly arisen mutant gene for haemophilia (bleeder's disease). The British Queen Victoria apparently arose from such a mutant sex cell; anyway, she transmitted the haemophilia gene through her daughters and granddaughters to the Russian and Spanish royalty. An irreverent scientist has even remarked that having been a carrier of a newly arisen mutant gene may eventually be the lady's chief claim to fame.

When all or a part of the victims of an hereditary disease regularly die without leaving progeny, and nevertheless the disease does not become less frequent with time, this is probably because the supply of diseased genes is kept up by mutation. When the number of the defective genes which are wiped out in every generation through death of their carriers without issue is equal to the number of these genes arising by mutation, the outgo and the income balance, the disease becomes neither more nor less frequent with time, and what is known as the state of equilibrium is established.

We can be absolutely sure that hereditary diseases and defects have not been brought about by the effects of civilized life. It is absurd to say that these diseases and defects indicate degeneration of the species. Natural populations of wild animals, as well as domestic animals, carry innumerable defective genes. There is no doubt that such "degeneration" has accompanied all evolution, including progressive evolution.

The Grain and the Chaff

As stated above, the occurrence of mutations is regarded in modern biology as the fountainhead of all evolution. In every generation, the process of mutation adds a variety of genes to the gene pool. Next, sexual reproduction and Mendelian recombination bring these genes into new combinations. And finally, natural selection is the great thresher, which separates the grain from the chaff. You may also liken organic evolution to the process of manufacture. Mutation supplies the raw materials, while sexual reproduction, Mendelian recombination, and natural selection accomplish the manufacturing process itself.

A seemingly very grave objection to this theory of evolution may have occurred to the reader. We have mentioned mutations which produce such serious hereditary diseases as haemophilia, or such traits as piebald skin, or woolly hair. If we were to describe more examples of mutations in various organisms, it would plainly appear that most of them are harmful, or at least useless, to their carriers. But harmful mutations can only lead to degeneration of the species; so how can such mutations improve the fitness of their possessors?

The solution of the puzzle is simple enough. In the above discussion we have forgotten an important variable—the environment. The fitness of carriers of a particular heredity may be low in some environments but high in others. In man, light-skinned, and especially albinotic, individuals often suffer painful sunburn, while persons with pigmented skin are relatively protected from this danger. On the other hand there is some evidence that light skins permit their possessors to secure a supply of vitamin D (the "sunlight" vitamin) more easily than do dark skins. Are, then, the genes which make the skin white useful or harmful? The question is evidently meaningless if the environment is not specified. Light pigmentation may be useful in countries with scarce sunshine, and dark pigmentation in climes with strong sunshine. The ability to withstand intense heat is very useful in the jungles of Africa or of Brazil; but it is resistance to cold which counts most with the inhabitants of Greenland or Tierra del Fuego. A group of botanists transplanted certain plants native on the seacoast of California to high mountain meadows; the transplanted individuals died because of their inability to stand the long mountain winters. On the other hand, when races of the same plant species which grow naturally on mountain meadows were transplanted to the coast, they proved very susceptible to attacks by a disease-producing fungus (mildew).

Some people like to believe that all men are born not only equal in rights but also biologically alike. But facts show clearly that people are not alike. And in the light of the evolution theory we can understand why men are not all alike. It is because the world in which we live is tremendously diversified. It has plains and mountains, woods, prairies, and deserts, rich and poor soil, tropical isles and arctic tundras, places where food is plentiful and others where it is difficult to come by. When a species is confronted with a variety of opportunities for life, it usually evolves a variety of types that are able to exploit these opportunities most efficiently. This diversification is made possible by the mutation process which furnishes the genetic raw materials from which diversity can be built.

A mutation may be harmful to its possessor in some

environments, say in cold climates, but useful in others, for example, in hot ones. This does not mean that every mutation must necessarily be useful in some environment. Most mutations, such as the human hereditary diseases discussed above, are injurious or even fatal in all known environments. Perplexing questions which may then be asked are these: Why should harmful and useful mutations occur indiscriminately at all times? Would it not be vastly more advantageous for life and for its evolution if only useful mutations were to take place only when and where they are needed? That would certainly spare mankind no end of the suffering caused by defective heredity.

The answers to these questions are not difficult. This is not a perfect world. Mutations are changes, probably chemical in nature, which alter the structure of the genes and their effects on body or mind. To produce only mutations that would be useful in the environment in which the descendants of a given individual are going to live would require the genes not only to possess wisdom but foresight. This is just too much to expect and, in any case, nature has not seen fit to endow mortal creatures with providential powers. All kinds of mutational changes of which a gene is capable do occur in it or in its descendants, given the vast stretches of time through which the hereditary material continues. A few of these changes will be useful to the organism in some environments. A majority of changes will be harmful, just because tinkering with a delicate mechanism is more likely to spoil it than to improve it. A more biological reason is that the mutations which are useful in today's environments took place in the past and have become incorporated in the "normal" hereditary constitution. The heredity which every one of us received is made up of mutations which occurred in our remote ancestors and which did prove more or less useful. For it is just this accumulation and combining of useful mutations which transformed our pre-human forebears into the human species.

Harmful mutations and hereditary diseases are thus the price which the species pays for the plasticity which makes continued evolution possible. A harsh and cruel price it is. It is for the human mind to seek to minimize this price, if it is not possible to do away with it altogether.

5. Controlling Man's Heredity

MAN is a relative newcomer on this earth. The most ancient fossil bones of men pretty much like the ones now living are only between 70 and 80 thousand years old. And the first light of recorded history dawned in Egypt and in Iraq only some six thousand years ago. On the time scale of biological evolution these are very recent dates, indeed. Some biological species have endured for many millions of years. And yet, the hereditary endowment of man, forged by natural selection, has enabled him to evolve his culture and to work tremendous changes on the face of the earth. He has modified profoundly many species of animals and plants which he has domesticated, has exterminated many wild species, and has altered the very appearance of a large portion of the land surface. Human civilization has proved to be a powerful agent not only biologically but even geologically.

One possession, however, man has neglected almost entirely. This is his most precious patrimony—his own hereditary endowment. This is not really surprising, because until very recently he knew very little about heredity. Acting on such insufficient and unreliable knowledge may well do much more harm than good. Although this knowledge still remains decidedly unsatisfactory nevertheless it has made rapid progress within the last century, and especially within the last decade or two. It is not premature, then, to think about the uses to which this knowledge should and should not be put.

Euthenics and Eugenics

No matter how much people disagree with each other about many things, they are unanimous in the recognition that the world in which we live is far from perfect and needs improvement. There is a distressing amount of disease, deformity and debility; individual humans do not always act as laudably, and human societies do not function as smoothly, as they should. The dissatisfaction with things as they are, and the ability to see things as they ought to be, are the prime movers of all progress. Now, there are two possible ways to change people (or other organisms). First, one can change the environments in which people grow up—the nutrition, sanitation, education, political systems, etc., so that people will be healthier, happier, more intelligent, and morally upright. This is euthenics. Secondly, one may strive to decrease the number of people born with hereditary defects of all kinds, and to increase the number with genes which favor the development of superior qualities. This is eugenics.

Eugenics and euthenics both aim to improve people. But euthenics proposes to work with existing genetic equipments, and to create environments in which the best potentialities of these equipments will be brought to realization. Eugenics aspires to alter the genetic basis of human populations and ultimately of mankind. It should be obvious that euthenics and eugenics are complementary and not conflicting modes of action. Unfortunately, they are all too frequently treated as alternatives. You may hear eloquent laments that individuals, groups, nations, or races are biologically primitive, tainted, or corrupt, so that all efforts spent on their education or on the improvement of their lot will be wasted. So, let us postpone any plans for social betterment till some vague future when inferior heredity will have been eliminated. Of course, the lamenters themselves, and the groups to which they belong, carry the most valuable genes, and they merit the best of living conditions, as well as a deciding voice in the fate of their less well endowed brethren. This attitude is all too frequently opposed by assertions that all will be well if we adopt some particular political nostrum, in complete disregard of the fact that some physical and mental illness is caused by defective heredity.

Here it must be emphasized again that heredity is not an implacable fate to which one must submit in resignation. Sugar diabetes is probably due to a defective gene, yet treatment with insulin makes the outward signs of the disease disappear. Moreover, many people who inherit the gene do not develop the disease. There can be no reasonable doubt that the progress of science will bring similar deliverance to sufferers from other hereditary diseases. A hereditary disease is not necessarily an incurable disease as is often wrongly supposed. After all, medicine is an applied science which proceeds to devise environments to which various human heredities would respond by production of the most favorable, or at any rate least objectionable, traits. Similarly, education aims, in the last analysis, to create environments in which the development of personalities would take the most favorable course. Theoretically, no heredity need be hopelessly beyond redemption. It is nevertheless true that for many hereditary diseases no treatments are yet in sight, and that individuals "cured" from diabetes transmit this gene to their offspring just as surely as do the actual sufferers.

Positive and Negative Eugenics

Eugenical measures may be positive and negative. Positive eugenics programs urge people who are regarded as carriers of desirable gene combinations to undertake the responsibilities of parenthood. Apart from propaganda designed to influence public opinion in desirable directions, positive eugenics favors economic measures which would ease the burdens of maternity and child care. A program of this kind has been in operation in Sweden since about 1937. It is premature to judge its genetic effects if any.

More enthusiasm has been shown in many places for negative eugenics, which urges elimination of undesirable genes by discouraging or making it impossible for persons who show the effects of such genes to have children. Since voluntary abstention from parenthood may be difficult, "sterilization" for individuals who are likely to have severe hereditary defects is recommended. Sterilization is accomplished through a surgical operation; the operated individuals are by no means "unsexed," show no outward signs of having undergone the treatment, but are unable to beget children. Sterilization laws are now on the statute books in many states and in some foreign countries. Some of them provide for sterilization only with the consent of the persons involved or of their guardians, others make it compulsory but controlled by the courts.

Many eugenists believe that putting this program into practice would improve the physical and mental qualities of mankind within a few generations, and some of the more enthusiastic ones have put forward quite extravagant claims. For example, one of the speakers at the International Congress of Eugenics held in New York in 1932 asserted that "there is no question that a sterilization law, enforced throughout the United States, would result, in less than one hundred years, in eliminating at least 90 per cent of crime, insanity, feeblemindedness, moronism, and abnormal sexuality, not to mention many other forms of defectiveness and degeneracy. Thus within a century, our asylums, prisons, and state hospitals would be largely emptied of their present victims of human woe and misery." However, let us not be carried away by big promises without a careful examination of the possibilities of their fulfillment.

Controlling Harmful Dominant Genes

The purpose of negative eugenics is to do away with hereditary diseases and other traits which are considered harmful or undesirable. There is no practical possibility of sending away the carriers of undesirable genes, since our neighbors probably would not desire to receive them either. The program of negative eugenics must, then, prevent or discourage child-bearing by the possessors of undesirable traits.

Nature itself applies the negative eugenics method to traits which are disabling or crippling. Many hereditary disabilities and diseases, which are clearly undesirable, like amaurotic idiocy in which the child loses its mind and goes blind, kill the persons who inherit them before they can have children. If a gene with such an effect is dominant, it will quickly be purged from the population, and its frequency in the population can only be maintained by new mutations of normal to abnormal genes (see p. 78).

But not all dominant abnormalities and diseases interfere with reproduction, and it is proposed to eliminate these by sterilizing or otherwise preventing the reproduction of persons who have such genes. Where such an undesirable trait can be diagnosed before the age of reproduction, and where it is certain that it is due to a defective gene, sterilization can be a dependable method for quickly getting rid of bad dominant genes. It obviously requires the consent of the state or other authority in preventing reproduction. If for some reason we should consider ability to taste PTC as undesirable and had the power to control human mating, we could easily produce a race which could not taste PTC. Tasting ability is, as we know, dominant. Just sterilize or otherwise prevent reproduction of all tasters and the job is done. Only non-tasters can have children and all their children will be non-tasters. The problem would seem to be solved in one generation.

In practice it is not quite so simple. Some persons with dominant hereditary afflictions may remain undetected and may thus slip through the sterilization dragnet. It has been supposed, for example, that only about 10 per cent of all the persons who inherit a dominant gene for diabetes actually develop the disease. A severe disease like Huntington's chorea (which is due to a dominant gene) often does not manifest itself until relatively late in life after the gene has already been passed on to the next generation. Nevertheless there is no doubt that prevention of reproduction on the part of possessors of bad dominant genes would quickly reduce the number of such genes.

But not all of bad heredity is due to simple dominant genes. Some hereditary abnormalities depend upon inter-actions between more than one gene and certain environmental conditions. Take for example "Mongoloid" idiocy. Many children with marks of this abnormality (short stature, broad skull, stubby hands, and other external features) are born each year. There are a number of cases in which both members of a pair of identical twins are idiots, while among fraternal twins it often happens that one is affected and the other is normal, suggesting that the disease is hereditary. It also tends to occur in more than one child in a family. It is possible that more than one gene, perhaps two different genes together, determine the abnormality. But the remarkable thing is that in a family with the hereditary tendency to produce "Mongoloid" children, it is much more frequent after the mother has passed the age of 35. There is something in the older mother that brings these genes to expression. Children of younger mothers undoubtedly inherit the same genes, but, since they are quite normal, they would escape any law designed to prevent the reproduction of such idiots.

Controlling Harmful Recessive Genes

The prospects for getting rid of bad heredity due to recessive genes are poorer than those for controlling undesirable dominant genes.

Here we must recall that every human being must fall into one of three categories in regard to each gene. We can call these categories AA, Aa and aa. If A stands for a dominant gene producing a certain trait, it can be recognized by its effects in AA and Aa people. But if the trait is recessive, like amaurotic idiocy, for example, it can be recognized only in the aa class, while it will be hidden in the Aa class. Now it happens that children afflicted with recessive diseases and abnormalities are born mostly to parents who are only heterozygous for the defective genes, and are themselves quite normal. Thus amaurotic idiots come only from *Aa* parents who are quite normal. That is to say, most of the recessive genes we might want to eliminate occur in hidden form in heterozygotes, in people who do not show them at all, instead of in homozygotes who could be identified and whose reproduction might consequently be prevented.

What proportions of the recessive genes are carried in hidden form in *Aa*, and in visible form in *aa* people depends on how common or how rare a given gene is in the population. Suppose that the genes *A* and *a* are equally frequent in the gene pool. In that case we find 25 per cent of *aa* and 50 per cent *Aa* individuals in the population, that is, twice as many *Aa* as *aa*. But when there are nine times as many *A* genes as *a*, then we find 81 per cent *AA*, 18 per cent *Aa*, and 1 percent *aa* individuals. Here, then, the heterozygotes are eighteen times more frequent than the recessive homozygotes. In general, the less frequent a recessive gene is in a population the more are the homozygotes outnumbered by heterozygotes. This should be clear from the following table which shows the relative numbers of *Aa* and *aa* people in the population with various proportions of the recessive gene in the gene "pool."

Per cent of gene in the gene pool	Per cent of *Aa* people	Per cent of *aa* people	Number of *Aa* people for each *aa* person
50	50	25	2
20	32	4	8
10	18	1	18
2	3.92	0.04	98
1	1.98	0.01	198
0.2	0.3992	0.0004	988
0.1	0.1998	0.0001	1998

This shows clearly that if a gene for a recessive disease

or abnormality is rare, nearly all of the genes will be found in *Aa* people who are themselves perfectly normal, although, of course, they transmit the disease to their off-spring. In England, for example, about one in every 20,-000 babies born is an albino. This means that in the gene pool a little more than ninety-nine percent of the genes are *A* (the gene for normal pigmentation) and less than one percent are *a* (the gene for albinism). In this case about one and a half per cent of people will be *Aa* (normally pigmented carriers of albinism). The carriers are, hence, about 280 times as numerous as are the albinos.

Now suppose that we are seized with a desire to have a race of people who can all taste PTC. Taste-blindness for PTC is to be regarded as a harmful trait, a defect which is to be purged from the race for good (actually, those who can taste PTC are, of course, neither superior nor inferior to those who can not). To realize this desire we should sterilize or otherwise prevent the taste-blind people from having children. Since taste-blindness be-haves in heredity as a recessive trait, all the taste-blind persons are in the *aa* category. Thus, we can stop all of the *a* genes in the *aa* people from going on to the next generation. But the gene for taste-blindness is found in *Aa* people as well, and *Aa* persons happen to be about twice as numerous as are *aa* people. Thus, even if all the taste-blind people are sterilized, the gene for taste-blind-ness will be perpetuated through the *Aa carriers*. Some taste-blind children will be born in the next generation.

The table below shows what would happen to a harm-ful recessive trait which to begin with shows in about 25 per cent of the population. This is only slightly below the actual frequency of taste-blindness in the United States. If all persons showing the recessive defect (*aa*) are sterilized generation after generation, the percentage of such defectives in the population will decline approxi-mately as follows:

Generation	Per cent of defectives
Initial	25
1	11
2	6
3	4
4	3
10	0.8
20	0.2
30	0.1
50	0.04
100	0.01

One generation after the introduction of the sterilization program the frequency of the defectives is cut to less than a half. So far, so good. But notice that to depress the frequency of the defectives from 6 to 3 per cent requires two generations. To reduce it further from 3 to about 1 per cent five generations will be needed. Ten more generations of an unrelenting sterilization program would carry the defectives down to 2 per 1000; ten more generations to 1 per thousand; seventy generations more to 1 per 10,000. The average length of a human generation is about 25 years. The reader can see for himself how much time is needed for the benefits of such a program to be felt.

A sterilization program directed against taste-blindness might make this trait much less frequent than it is now within about a century. Now, let us turn to our program against albinism, a recessive trait which is to begin with much less common in human populations than taste-blindness. As stated above, *Aa* carriers are about 280 times more frequent in the population than *aa* albinos. There are about 1400 *Aa* carriers and only 5 *aa* albinos per 100,-000 people in the population, that is, 1410 *a* genes per 198,590 normal, *A* genes. In sterilizing the five albinos we are doing away with 10 *a* genes, and hereby reduce the total number of *a* genes in one generation from 1410 to just 1400. This represents virtually no progress at all in getting rid of albinism. It would take about 58 generations (some 1450 years!) to reduce the proportion of albinos in the population to half the present frequency.

Now the full meaning of the above table becomes apparent in practical terms. Where a recessive gene is common, it is frequently present in the *aa* form, that is, in people who actually show its effects, its frequency could be quickly reduced by preventing the reproduction of *aa* people. But as the recessive genes become rare, sterilization programs become less and less effective.

Now, we have tacitly assumed that the sterilization program is absolutely thorough, so that not a single defective ever escapes sterilization. It is, of course, doubtful if any program could be so airtight in practice. But even if we were able to enforce complete compliance with a sterilization program, the dependence of the effects of genes on the environment would be another stumbling block. We have already discussed this matter in connection with the sterilization of carriers of undesirable dominant genes (p. 86). The progress is much slowed down if some individuals with defective heredity are normal in appearance and, therefore, escape sterilization.

Assume, for example, that in a certain population 10 per cent (1000 per 10,000) of individuals have a recessive defect. If all such individuals are eliminated from parenthood, the frequency of the defect in the next generation will be reduced to 576 per 10,000. But if only half of them are eliminated, the defect will appear in 790 per 10,000; if only 10 per cent are sterilized the defect will be present in 961 individuals out of each 10,000.

This impotence of programs of negative eugenics to cope with rare defects is stressed for the very good reason that, strange as it may seem, genes for most hereditary defects are individually rare. This surely does not mean that there is little human wretchedness in the world, or for that matter little wretchedness due to defective heredity. But the fact is that there are so many *different* defects that relatively little can be blamed on each one taken separately. For example, no fewer than 100 different hereditary eye diseases are known, so that the incidence of most of them taken separately is quite low.

Mental diseases present a human problem even more serious than blindness. Here again, a certain proportion of cases have little or nothing to do with heredity. Cases attributable to defective heredity are of many kinds which can be more or less easily distinguished by a specialist and are almost certainly due to different genes. Each gene is rare if its frequency is computed for the total population of the country, and progress in reducing the frequency of each one separately will be very slow. This is a great difficulty which advocates of sterilization do not always take account of.

Difficulties of Eugenics

We have seen that the efficacy of negative eugenics programs is by no means as great as claimed by some of their overenthusiastic supporters. Only if a defect is due to a single dominant gene the presence of which in a person is easily recognizable would elimination of all the defectives lead to disappearance of the defect in the following generation, except for new mutations. But it is doubtful if any eugenic sterilization program could be so thorough in practice, and one must reckon that only a fraction of the defectives would be prevented from reproduction in every generation. Moreover, the defect might develop in only some environments, and therefore a more or less considerable proportion of the carriers of the dominant defective genes would escape being identified as such. The usefulness of the eugenic program is thereby lessened still further. Nevertheless, where dominant defective genes are involved, elimination of their carriers from parenthood would unquestionably benefit the coming generations.

Where defects due to recessive genes are concerned the efficiency of sterilization is in general low. Only if a recessive defect is very common in the population can sterilization of all the afflicted persons produce a substantial decrease of their numbers in the next generation. For defects which are rare, or caused by recessive genes which show only in certain environments, or dependent on two or more recessive genes present in the same individual, very little is accomplished by sterilizing even all the defectives in a single generation. To be sure, if a sterilization program is continued for many generations, the defect will become eventually less common than it was to begin with. The process may, however, take centuries or even millennia. There is, however, a way to increase the efficacy of efforts to reduce the frequency of deleterious recessive genes and that is to find means of detecting them in heterozygotes or carriers in whom the gene does not produce the defect. This calls for more vigorous research on the detection of carriers.

Our opinion regarding the worthwhileness of such a program will depend on how dear to us is the comfort of remote posterity compared to the discomfort of our contemporaries. It is, perhaps, not too selfish to say that posterity should be allowed to tackle its own problems and to hope that it may have better means for doing so than we have. The discovery of such means is already under way. The difficulty with recessive defective genes is that a single dose of such a gene does not produce the defect in the carrier (heterozygote). The problem then is to identify such carriers. It is already possible to do this in the case of a gene which in homozygous state causes a blood disease (Cooley's anemia) which is fatal in early life. Persons who carry the gene for sickle cell anemia, also fatal when homozygous, can now be accurately identified. Extension of this ability, which depends only on the progress of research, will make it possible to advise carriers of the same recessive defect of the risk they will run if they have children; or where necessary to advise sterilization of carriers of severe defects, and thus make a sterilization program really effective. Finally, let us not forget that treatments may and probably will be found that will relieve or cancel the manifestation of hereditary defects, as insulin relieves the manifestation of hereditary diabetes.

On the other hand, it is possible to argue that, even though a eugenical program is of little effectiveness as far as mankind as a whole is concerned, it is worth while if it prevents the misery of a single or several human individuals being born with grave defects. On this basis, abstention from parenthood of persons who are likely to transmit defective genes can only be welcomed, especially if this abstention is voluntary. What has to be very carefully watched is that eugenical programs of various kinds should not be substituted for measures designed to improve the living conditions and the opportunities of people to secure their share of happiness in life.

Radiation Hazards

No eugenics program can eliminate all hereditary diseases and genetic defects, because defective genes arise from normal ones by mutation, as set forth in Chapter 4. Mutation, of course, generates good genes also, but for reasons already discussed most mutations are harmful. Now, every harmful mutation will eventually cause a "genetic death" of a human individual, although this may occur many generations after the origin of the mutation, especially if the mutation is recessive. We must, then, do all in our power to diminish the number of defective mutant genes being added to the gene pool of human populations. Unfortunately, the progress of modern science and technology has so far accomplished the exact opposite—the rate of origin of harmful mutations is likely to become very much increased.

The use of X rays for diagnostic and therapeutic purposes is among the important tools of modern medicine. It happens, however, that X rays are also the most powerful known means for increasing the frequency of mutations. If, then, insufficient care is exercised, so that the sex glands (ovaries or testes) of the patient are irradiated when the patient is treated with X rays, mutations will be induced in some of his sex cells. The insidious nature of this hazard is that it is completely imperceptible either to the patient or to the physician. But if the patient becomes a parent he is likely to transmit a mutant gene to his offspring. If this gene is dominant, the child is born with some defect, which will in all likelihood not be ascribed to the treatment at all. But if the mutation is recessive, then several or even many generations may elapse before the harm becomes apparent.

The release of atomic energy, either for constructive or for destructive ends, will expose to mutation-inducing radiations even greater numbers of people. Of course, if the sex glands are shielded from the radiations used for medical purposes, or produced in atomic energy plants, the danger of harmful mutations in the sex cells may be reduced. One must only remember that there is no such thing as a "safe" dose of radiation; the number of mutations induced is simply proportional to the amount of radiation reaching the sex cells, and if a person is exposed daily to small amounts of the rays, these small amounts may add up to very dangerous sums.

Misuse of atomic energy may result in eventual harm to mankind which is fearful to contemplate. If atomic weapons are resorted to in major wars, large masses of humanity will unavoidably be exposed to mutation-inducing radiations. Persons killed or maimed will be the obvious victims, but those who survive will transmit to their immediate and remote progeny some defective heredity which will add to human misery during centuries and perhaps during millennia. The defective genes introduced into the human gene pool will be doing their gruesome work in a slow but remorseless way. Those in whose power it lies to plunge mankind into this calamity, or to save it from this trial, should be made conscious of the magnitude of their responsibility. They do not show this consciousness now.

Differential Fertility

Accurate statistics of births and deaths in the United States exist for less than a century. Nevertheless, it is certain that in colonial days an American woman gave birth to between two and three times as many babies in her lifetime as does her modern descendant. Even in 1800, there were close to one thousand children under five years old per one thousand women of reproductive age in the American population. By 1930, this figure stood at about four hundred children per one thousand women. The birth rates have declined within the last century or two not only in the United States but in other civilized countries as well. Most people feel this decline to be salutary, except where (as in France and some other European countries) it reached such a stage that the populations began to shrink below what is regarded as optimal sizes. For simultaneously with the reduction of births, the infant mortality and the general death rates have declined also. With improved techniques of child care and the advances in general hygiene, a smaller number of babies suffices to keep the population replacing itself in each generation. As a matter of fact, it is the high birth rate in overpopulated countries like China, India, Japan, Egypt, or Puerto Rico, that causes deep concern.

Careful examination of the shrinking birth rates has, however, revealed a circumstance that is also unfortunate. Namely, the shrinkage has been strongest among just those social groups and classes which should be best qualified to furnish decent upbringing to their offspring. Thus, women with better schooling and education should make more desirable mothers than ignorant or uninformed women. Yet, women aged 45–59 years had the following average numbers of children:

Mother's Schooling	Children
None	3.95
1-4 years of grade school	4.33
5-6 years of grade school	3.74

7-8 years of grade school 2.78
1-3 years of high school 2.37
 4 years of high school 1.75
1-3 years of college 1.71
 4 years of college 1.23

In 1935, families with annual incomes below $1000 had on the average about twice as many children as those with incomes between $1500 and $2000; and these latter families had some fifty per cent more children than families with annual incomes of $3000 and over. Farm laborers had more children than farm owners; unskilled workers more than skilled ones; and professional and business groups had fewest children of all.

There is some evidence that things may have changed since 1935, when a severe economic depression was forcing some people to refrain from having children. In the United States, the birth rates have increased since World War II, and this increase is observed in families with high, as well as with low, incomes. Nevertheless, it continues to be true that more prosperous families tend to produce fewer children than do the less prosperous ones.

Now, it happens that just these groups which have greater average numbers of children show, when tested by psychologists, lower average "intelligence quotients" (I.Q.) than groups with fewer children. For example, the following average I.Q.'s were found by Hagerty and Nash (in 1924) among children whose fathers belong to these different occupational groups:

Occupation of the Father

	Average I.Q. of Children
Professional	116
Business, Clerical	107
Skilled Trades	98
Semi-Skilled	95
Farmers	91
Unskilled Labor	89

The observed differential fertility of social classes is unfortunate, quite regardless of whether human intelligence is or is not influenced by heredity. It stands to reason that an intelligent mother is better qualified to bring up children than a dull one; that a well-educated mother is more desirable than an ignorant one, and that a family of means can provide better upbringing for its children than a family of paupers. But some writers have conjured out of these facts an apocalyptic vision which, if it were true, would make the future of mankind bleak indeed.

Are People Getting More Stupid?

The gloomy argument runs about as follows. On the average, more children per family are born in some social classes than in others. Future generations will be descended to a greater extent from the more fertile than from the less fertile people. Now, the more fertile classes are lower in average intelligence than the less fertile groups. The more intelligent people have, in effect, partly sterilized themselves by leaving the business of childbearing chiefly to the less well-endowed groups. Although human intelligence is partly dependent on environmental opportunity, there is good evidence (see Chapter 2) that it is influenced also by the heredity of different persons. If so, the average intelligence of coming generations will be less than that of the present time. It has even been calculated that the average I.Q. of the American population shrinks by about one I.Q. "point" per generation. Other authorities are still more pessimistic and expect a decline by between 2 and 4 "points" per generation. We are being transformed into "a nation of congenital morons." R. C. Cook expects that "The machinery of a complex culture would begin to break down."

Is this doom inevitable? Studies on twins have, to be sure, shown the existence of a genetic component in the development of human intelligence. But is it justified to conclude from the twin studies that the differences in I.Q. averages observed between, say, workers and businessmen have the same genetic component? Persons within a social class may be genetically different, for example, in eye color or in intelligence; but it does not follow that the different social classes must necessarily show a different incidence of individuals with different eye colors or different intelligence. To prove that the I.Q. differences between social classes are genetic, one would have to furnish complete equality of opportunity to children of all social classes and to observe the results for, preferably, several generations. Of course, no such experiment has been done.

Nevertheless, another large scale experiment has been carried out, which gives no support to the dire predictions that people will become duller and more slow-witted with every generation. In 1932, and again in 1947, I.Q. tests were administered to 11-year-old children in Scotland. The numbers of the children tested were 87,498 in 1932 and 70,805 in 1947. These numbers are estimated to represent 87 and 88 per cent of all children of the age studied who lived in Scotland at the times when the tests were made. There is, then, no question that the results obtained give a fair measure of the average I.Q. of 11-year-old Scottish children. It should also be noted that in Scotland, as in the United States and in some other countries, children from less prolific families showed higher average I.Q.'s than those from more prolific ones. Thus, the average I.Q. of single children was 113, while that of children who had five brothers and sisters was only 91. This tendency for children from larger families to have lower I.Q.'s was observed within the more prosperous, as well as among the less prosperous, social groups. No wonder, then, that the average I.Q. was expected to be lower in 1947 than it was in 1932. The facts showed, however, the exact opposite; the average score for 1947 proved to be 2.2 points *higher* than in 1932.

Even though we cannot conclude that the Scottish children are becoming brighter with time, surely there is no basis to think that the biological forces which operate in our society lead to deterioration of the intelligence. There are several loopholes in the reasoning which leads some people to expect such deterioration. Better educated mothers and fathers have fewer children not necessarily *because* they are better educated. It is also possible that some parents are better educated because they have fewer children. Early marriage obviously favors greater fecundity, and early marriage may interfere with the completion of a course of education. And vice versa, a willingness to postpone the satisfactions of marriage and family life often makes it easier to acquire an education. Again, the responsibilities of family life may restrict the freedom of movement of the parents, and thus interfere with their upward progress on the social ladder and with the growth of their annual income. Statistics show that families who live in low rental homes have on the average more children than families who occupy better homes. But it does not necessarily follow that poor housing favors childbearing, because families with many children may sometimes be forced to occupy more modest dwellings. Some people have been notoriously rash in giving biological interpretations to social and economic facts.

Acquired Characters

The sound core of eugenics is that it draws attention to the need of scientific study of the human gene pool, and of practical measures to control the contents of this pool in the best interests of mankind. Unfortunately, eugenics has often been perverted to a pseudoscientific justification of social inequalities and oppression. It is common knowledge that complete equality of opportunity does not exist in the United States or in other western democratic countries. In much of Europe and of Latin America the social stratification is discouragingly rigid. And anyone familiar with the social conditions of the East can not forget the degrading poverty of the teeming masses, contrasted with the extravagant luxury of a small minority. The notion that the underprivileged classes are biologically inferior to the favored ones is merely a convenient but specious vindication of the inequality which in any case is not biologically inevitable.

Now, those who have urged social reforms for the relief of human suffering have sometimes fallen prey to another biological delusion. It is an attractive idea that the improvements gained by one generation in health and culture and education would pass automatically to the next generations. The idea also appeals to some that if all people were subjected to the same conditions they would all become alike. The question, however, is not whether we may wish this to be so, but whether it is so. Many studies made by many investigators have produced no evidence whatever that bodily or mental traits acquired by the parents are passed on to the children through biological heredity. As we know, heredity determines not traits themselves, but responses of the individual to his environment. When a parent responds in a given way to his environment, the responses of his children are not thereby modified. Educational achievements of the parents are not inherited by the children; children have to be educated for themselves. Neither do we inherit the acquired vices of our parents nor the changes in their bodies and minds brought about by accidents, malnutrition, sorrow, and the like.

The notion that acquired characters are inherited is very old. In fact, it started not as a scientific theory at all but as a widespread popular belief. It is explicitly stated in the Bible, in the story of Jacob's experiments in the production of ringstreaked, speckled, and spotted sheep, that the conditions to which parents are exposed determine some of the characters of the progeny which are subsequently inherited. Later this idea became associated with the name of Lamarck, the pioneer French evolutionist. Lamarck knew that bodily parts, such as muscles, are strengthened by use and exercise, and are weakened by prolonged disuse. He supposed that evolution occurs because animals make efforts to secure food, to escape from enemies, and the like, and in so doing exercise and develop specific parts of their bodies. For example, Lamarck supposed that the giraffe got his long neck because the remote ancestors of the giraffe stretched their necks in the efforts to get at the foliage of tall trees on which these animals feed. The crucial question is whether the offspring of those giraffes which stretched their necks most are born with longer necks than they would otherwise have had. Strange as it may seem, Lamarck did not raise this question at all—he took it for granted that the stretching would be inherited.

Darwin supposed that evolution occurs by means of natural selection (see Chapter 4). For example, the giraffe's neck became long because the individuals with somewhat longer necks secured more abundant food and had on the average more progeny than the relatively short-necked individuals. Nevertheless, Darwin shared the belief, which was universal in his day, that acquired traits are inherited. He even invented what he himself called a "provisional hypothesis of pangenesis" to visualize how such inheritance might take place. According to this hypothesis, every part of the body prepares a kind of diminutive copy of itself, which he called a "pangene." These "pangenes" are transported by blood to the sex glands, where they unite to form the sex cells. A body part which has acquired a new character, say an arm the muscles of which have been strengthened by exercise, will bud off an altered "pangene," and this "pangene" will produce a modified organ in the progeny.

Darwin knew that his hypothesis of pangenesis was just a guess; this is why he stressed its provisional character. But it fulfilled the most important function of any scientific hypothesis: it stimulated a great amount of research and experimentation. For at least thirty years, many biologists, among whom the names of Weismann and Galton should be mentioned most prominently, made studies on plants and animals to see whether acquired characters are ever inherited. The number of believers in this contingency dwindled steadily, because the outcome of the experiments on inheritance of acquired characters was so uniformly negative.

The rediscovery of Mendel's laws and the development of genetics in the current century have produced a much better understanding of the mechanism of heredity than was available in Darwin's and Weismann's day. In the light of this understanding we can clearly see why acquired characters are not inherited. This is because heredity is transmitted through genes and not through blood mixtures (see Chapter 3). Genes arise *from each other* by division, they are not made in the various organs of the body as "pangenes" and not transported into the reproductive parts and into the sex cells. The genes appear to be chemical molecules which reproduce themselves from the environment, from food. The development of the body is ultimately a by-product of gene reproduction, and not vice versa.

The most recent recrudescence of belief in the inheritance of acquired characters with its supporting machinery of pangenes occurred in the Soviet Union in the 1930's and 1940's. There an agronomist, Lysenko, set out to discredit the chromosomal theory of heredity and to substitute ideas resting on claims that heredity can be changed by the conditions under which a plant grows, or by influences from the stock of one variety on grafts upon it from another variety. When Lysenko's experiments, from which the above conclusions were drawn, were repeated by experimenters outside the Soviet Union, the results contradicted Lysenko's assertions. Nevertheless, his views were endorsed by the Communist Party, and Western or "bourgeois" genetics was outlawed. There are signs that this attitude is relaxing, but nevertheless the potential contributions of Soviet biology to genetics have been suppressed for nearly twenty years, and what is more important for that country, potential contributions to the improvement of the plants and animals on which its agricultural progress depends have been suspended. There is no doubt that the laws of heredity operate alike in different parts of the world. Political interference affects not their truth but their application for the benefit of man.

Bodily or mental traits acquired during an individual's life are not transmitted to his offspring. The refutation of the view that acquired characters are inherited has, however, been widely misunderstood as meaning that the heredity, the genes, are unchangeable or somehow insulated from the environment. It must be admitted that the language used by some early geneticists was conducive to such misunderstanding, and this gave to Lysenko the pretext to declare the theory of the gene "mystical" and even "pseudo-scientific."

That genes can be changed by the environment is indeed self-evident. Although the exact chemical make-up of the genes is not known, they consist of a kind of chemical substance (nucleo-protein) which is extremely complex and can undergo changes in many ways. To give a crude example, when you boil eggs for your breakfast, you surely change the genes contained in these eggs by heat. Or, you can kill the sex cells of any organism by any one of a great variety of poisons, and this will also change the genes carried in these sex cells. The important problem is evidently not whether genes can be changed, for they clearly can be, but what are the consequences of the change. And here it appears that the most usual result of changing the gene is to kill it. This is really not surprising at all, if one remembers that the gene is like a very delicate mechanism, and as such it is most likely to be spoiled by any shock. Nobody expects to improve his watch by poking a stick into its mechanism. The changes in the gene which are interesting to us are of a very special kind: They must be retained when the gene reproduces itself by making its copy from outside materials, from food. Such changes are called mutations (see Chapter 4), and they occur relatively rarely. The statement that the heredity of an organism can not be changed easily means, then, only that we do not yet know how to make the genes of a certain kind mutate to a desired alternative state.

But even the lack of control over the mutation process does not mean that the heredity can not be changed by the environment or by human effort. The hereditary endowment of any organism, including man, is an outcome of an evolutionary development controlled by natural selection (see Chapter 4). Now, natural selection is an agency of the environment, which changes the heredity by a subtle but nonetheless very effective method: by letting the well-adapted organisms survive and reproduce, and by failing to perpetuate the genetic endowments which are out of tune with their environment. Man has followed the example of nature when he changed, by artificial selection, the heredity of his domesticated animals and plants to serve his needs or fancy. And the obstacles in the way of the application of similar methods to the control of man's own heredity are chiefly sociological, not biological, in origin.

6. Race

IT IS AN old human habit to believe that one's own family or race is better than the neighbors, but it is a relatively new idea to ascribe this superiority to inherited biological qualities. The Greeks of more than 2,000 years ago felt quite sure that they were better than barbarians, barbarians being generously defined as all non-Greeks; but they regarded the barbarian as inferior not because there was anything wrong with his body, but because his table manners, so to speak, were so bad. The Greeks could also detect the same superior attitude in other peoples of antiquity. As far back as the fifth century B.C. Herodotus, the great historian, wrote with subtle irony that Persians "look upon themselves as very greatly superior in all respects to the rest of mankind, regarding others as approaching to excellence in proportion as they dwell nearer to them; whence it comes to pass that those who are the farthest off must be the most degraded of mankind."

Later, it was not a Roman "race" that ruled so much of the civilized world but Roman ideas of government, Roman law, Roman discipline and military achievement; and many a "barbarian" acquired this belief in Roman superiority by becoming a Roman citizen.

Mohammedans are often, though quite wrongly, regarded as intolerant, yet they always accepted without discrimination anyone who embraced their religion. The early Christians in general adopted the same attitude, paying little attention to biological or racial differences, since they regarded as fundamental those differerences in behavior which, like those of the Pharisees, arose from differences in beliefs.

In medieval lore one of the three wise men who came

107

to Christ in Bethlehem was pictured as a Negro. As recently as 250 years ago Peter the Great of Russia imported, among other marvels, a Negro boy. This lad had a hard time convincing a prospective Russian father-in-law that in spite of the blackness of his skin he was not related to the devil, but eventually he married into the Russian aristocracy, and his great-grandson, Alexander Pushkin, became the greatest of Russian poets and one of the great poets of the world.

The idea of biological superiority based on race appears in the Old Testament. Here it is quite clear that Jehovah made his covenant with Abraham and "with his seed," that is, with those descended biologically from Abraham. In the New Testament there are vivid descriptions of the conflict between this view and the radical, even revolutionary, doctrine of the universal brotherhood of man.

The issue is still joined. Many people declare it to be the "white man's burden" to rule men of all other colors. And so anxious have some white men been to lay this burden upon themselves that they used their superior weapons to fight and kill colored people, and incidentally other whites, for this privilege. Again it became useful to the German Nazis to think that their neighbors were biologically degraded. The world could only be benefited by the killing of Slavs and Jews and other "inferior races." Truly, race superiority is very useful when armies are on the march.

But if ideas about war and conquest are as old as history, at least one factor has come into the world in recent times. This is the knowledge of human races and of human biology which is emerging from the studies of many scientists specializing in this subject. Military leaders and politicians have been learning how to use real or assumed scientific discoveries to add an appearance of respectability to their propaganda. Such propaganda, even when directed to evil ends, can not accomplish its purpose if we know the facts of human biology. What then is the truth about race? What has science to say about it?

Race Classification

About one fact of cardinal importance practically all scientists are agreed: All men belong to a single species, and there are no divisions between any varieties of men like those barriers which separate the species of animals. All kinds of human beings can mate and have offspring, regardless of geographic origin, color, or other biological difference. All have the same general characteristics, which caused the first great classifier of animals and plants, the Swedish naturalist Linnaeus, in 1738 to assign all men to the species *Homo sapiens* (Homo for *man*, sapiens for *wise*, an opinion which we should probably only dare express in Latin!). Linnaeus placed this species at the pinnacle of the animal kingdom.

Linnaeus knew, of course, that the men who inhabit the different parts of the world are not all alike, and so he divided the human species into four varieties, as follows:

americanus (American Indian)—Tenacious, contented, free; ruled by custom

europaeus—Light, lively, inventive; ruled by rites

asiaticus—Stern, haughty, stingy; ruled by opinion

afer (African)—Cunning, slow, negligent; ruled by caprice

The first classification was, as we see, based on characters of the mind and not of the body. The fault of this classification was that it didn't classify: contented, lively and negligent people can be found everywhere.

A little later (1775) the German scholar Blumenbach, founder of anthropology, the scientific study of man, proposed to divide men according to skin color into five varieties and to each of these varieties was given the name "race," a term which had been employed earlier by the French scientist Buffon. The five "races" of Blumenbach were:

Caucasian or white

Mongolian or yellow

Ethiopian or black
American or red
Malayan or brown

This was a biological classification which obviously described existing differences between large populations inhabiting different parts of the world.

Other anthropologists thought that skin color was too superficial a trait and they resorted to measurements of parts and proportions of the body, particularly of the head. Races were recognized by head shape in conjunction with particular combinations of other traits, nearly all of which were present to some degree in all "races" and which were not constant with any race. Head shape as we know may differ sharply within the same family, even among brothers and sisters.

The use of such methods led to a great multiplication of races. Deniker in 1889 recognized 29 of them distinguished by hair form, with skin color and nose shape as subsidiary traits. In 1933 von Eickstedt set up three basic races, "Europid," "Negrid" and "Mongolid," with 18 "subraces," 3 "collateral races," 11 "collateral subraces" and 3 "intermediate forms." In 1950, the American anthropologists Coon, Garn, and Birdsell, recognized 6 "putative stocks"—Negroid, Mongoloid, White, Australoid, American Indian, and Polynesian—and 30 different races.

No agreement has emerged from such efforts as to what constitutes a race. The confusion is made worse by those who fail to distinguish groups resembling each other biologically from those united in a national or language community. "American" as applied to citizens of the United States can certainly designate no biological unit. There is no "American race" (unless it be the red men displaced by the immigrants from Europe); nor is there a Swiss race or a French race. A nation may consist of more than one race, and several nations, like those of the British Commonwealth, may be biologically alike. The inhabitants of northern Germany resemble physically the inhabitants of Denmark and Sweden more than they do the South Germans, who in turn are physically similar to some Frenchmen, Czechs and Yugoslavs. You will not be able to distinguish by sight some Swedes, Finns and Russians, yet they speak very different languages.

It is very easy to be deceived by differences amongst peoples even more superficial and easily acquired than language or ideas or religion. Dress and decoration, even hair-do, may make some people seem dissimilar as a group from the very population from which they are descended. If one were to arrange a guessing contest as to what "race" certain particular Europeans belong to, it would have to be conducted either without any clothing or decoration at all or with the neutral uniform of dress and hair style which the clothiers and permanent wavers of the city are spreading throughout all populations. "Racial" differences have often been inferred from characters almost as transitory as these.

The misuse of "race" for political and military purposes has brought the term "race" into such disrepute that many people, including some scientists, propose to abandon the term altogether as applied to human groups. It is true that it is used in many ways. By "the human race" we certainly do not mean the same thing as "the races of man"; nor does the latter convey the same meaning of race as is intended in a discussion of the "races of Europe"; and yet there are human entities for which the term race, if properly used, could stand.

If change of name could cure some of the ills which the race notion, or rather the misuses of that notion, have brought about, then it might be better to convey the idea of race in other words. Some have used "ethnic group" in place of race; but unfortunately "ethnic group prejudice" is easily exchangeable for "race prejudice"; and one can hate "ethnic groups" just as venomously as real or imaginary races.

Any one can see that the inhabitants of Chinatown differ in appearance from those living on Park Avenue, and that Pullman porters as a group differ from train conductors as a group. These are facts which require expression and understanding, and they will not disappear behind a changed name. There is no doubt that the popular idea of race as well as that held by the older anthropology are both invalid, but it takes some effort to see where the fallacy lies.

How Races Are Distinguished

How does a layman and how does a scientist arrive at the idea of race? Suppose that we consider the inhabitants of an American city, such as New York. We know the different kinds of people who live in different sections of the city, in Harlem, in Little Italy, in the Norwegian colony in Brooklyn, and so on. As laymen we recognize the facial and bodily traits which are usual in the different groups. In Harlem the majority of people have dark skins, tightly curled hair, broad noses and thick lips, and we know that these have come from African ancestors. In the Norwegian colony we find many tall people, many blonds, and many with blue eyes; whereas those of Italian descent tend to be shorter, brunet and dark-eyed. Amongst those of South German or Swiss descent we are more likely to find medium stature, brown hair, fair skin, and round heads.

We might conclude that among these neighbors in the city we can identify four groups or races: African, north European, central European and south European. Some anthropologists have called these Negro, Nordic, Alpine, and Mediterranean. If asked to describe what Negroes or Nordics are like we may make a sort of composite picture of all the Negroes or all the Nordics that we know; or we may pick out one or a few individuals who have struck us as "typical" and describe their qualities as those of Negroes and Nordics in general.

The anthropologist has generally used refinements of these methods. He has combined the measurements and descriptive notes taken on a number of persons of a certain group and has calculated the *average* stature, average head shape, and the averages of other bodily characters. He gives this set of averages as the characteristic of the group.

At this point, whether we have reached it by "scientific" or by laymen's methods, the trouble begins. In the first place, we may make the mistake which has been so common in the past, of assuming some necessary connection between the physical characters which we have observed or measured and mental and cultural characters of the group. The skin color, hair shape and lip thickness of Negroes is known to be inherited and to develop as well in northern Harlem as in equatorial Africa. It is known also that most northern Negroes live in slums, enjoy jazz and engage in manual or menial labor. One is likely to jump to the conclusion that the economic and social and cultural position of the Negro is also inherited and will continue regardless of education and opportunity. But it is obvious this does not follow from the facts at all.

Difficulties of Race Classification

If we avoid succumbing to the above error, we must then learn to resist the temptation, which is even stronger, to identify individuals with races. Negroes and Nordics and Alpines differ *as groups,* but mistakes are bound to be made if one tries to place every person that one meets in one of these groups. Perhaps not many mistakes will be made in assigning persons to the Negro group on the one hand or to the Nordic on the other; but a veritable avalanche of mistakes will be made in trying to separate Nordics, Alpines and Mediterraneans. Anthropologists armed with all their measurements are in little better position than the layman when it comes to deciding to which of these European "races" a given person belongs. The averages may describe very well the ideal Nordic or Alpine, but ideals and averages are abstractions, and it is just a lucky accident if the person whose race we wish to determine happens to have all his traits coincide exactly with the averages for any one race. If we make many measurements and calculate averages for all of them we may find ourselves in the predicament that no actually existing man or woman of any race anywhere conforms to the race ideal. Since every individual differs from any other individual, everyone belongs to his own special race; but to say that makes the race concept absurd.

Not only individuals but also whole groups of people are frequently difficult to place in any one race. Our ideas about Nordics come from our acquaintance with Norwegians and Swedes, and our ideas about the Alpines from observations on southern Germans. Now, inhabitants of northern and central Germany are on the whole intermediate between Nordics and Alpines; yet, among them individuals may be found who are just as "typical" Nordics and "typical" Alpines as can be found anywhere. What race do these people belong to? We may try to escape the difficulty by saying that both Nordic and Alpine "bloods flow in their veins," or simply that they are racial mixtures or hybrids. But a moment's reflection will show that this leads into another difficulty no less serious than the first.

Pure Races?

If you say that something is a mixture, you imply that pure ingredients which have been mixed together either exist somewhere, or have existed in the past. But where are the pure Nordics, pure Alpines, pure Mediterraneans, etc.? Wherever you go, you find that only very few, if any, inhabitants of a country conform to any possible notion of racial purity and uniformity. For example, you will meet a lot of tall, blond and blue-eyed persons in the city of Oslo, Norway, but you will find there also many individuals with brown eyes and dark hair. There is nothing to indicate that the possessors of these un-Nordic colorations are any less native to the city than are the blue-eyed blonds. Similarly, blue-eyed blonds are met with occasionally among Spaniards, most of whom are brunets.

As a last resort, one may suppose that, although no countries inhabited by "pure" Nordics and "pure" Alpines (or by any other "pure" race for that matter) exist at present, such countries did exist in the past. This supposition is actually implied in most popular discussions of the "race problem." Back in some distant Golden Age people zealously kept their race "pure," and this made them strong and wise. Recently they allowed themselves to become mixed or "mongrelized," and the twilight of humanity is about to swallow us as a consequence. Such notions are, however, definitely refuted by scientific data. Race mixture has been going on during the whole of recorded history. Incontrovertible evidence from studies on fossil human remains shows that even in prehistory, at the very dawn of humanity, mixing of different stocks (at least occasionally) took place. Mankind has always been, and still is, a mongrel lot.

To be sure, the growth of the world's population in the last two hundred years, coupled with the development of the means of travel and communication, has enormously speeded up the process of mixing of the human races. Mixing of at least closely related races (such as those living in different European countries) appears, however, to be biologically desirable rather than the reverse. A gradual increase of the average stature has been going on in most civilized countries of the world during at least the last hundred years. This becoming taller is due in part to improvement of hygienic conditions and to better nutrition, but in part also to the lifting of barriers which in the past separated different peoples so that "tall" genes could spread more widely. However that may be, nothing can be more certain than that pure races in man never existed and can not exist.

But suppose that the population of a country, a city, or an island were isolated from any immigrants from the outside and allowed to breed for many generations within itself, would not this population eventually become a "pure" race? Here we come to a matter of crucial importance for the understanding of the whole problem of race. "Pure" races could exist only if heredity were like a fluid transmitted through "blood," and if the hereditary "bloods" of the parents mixed and fused in their offspring. We know that this does not happen. The experiments of Mendel and the calculations of

Hardy and Weinberg showed that heredity is transmitted not as fluids which can be mixed and diluted, but in discrete packages called genes, so that a child inherits just ½ of the genes each of its parents possesses, and that brothers and sisters receive different sets of genes. The old race notion is based on the "blood" theory of heredity; and the old idea of race is just as fallacious as the blood theory.

Suppose that individuals with blue eyes and blond hair, and with dark eyes and black hair, exist in a certain population. If the hereditary "bloods" were to mix, all individuals in this population would eventually show a uniform mixture of light and dark complexion; they would all have light brown eyes and hair. Actually the genes for the different eye and hair colors do not mix. Populations descended from Europeans will always have individuals with dark and light brown and blue eyes, and with black, brown, and blond hair. They will always stay mixed, and will never become uniform or "pure."

When a trait, such as the skin color in Negroes and whites, is determined by cooperation of several genes, it may seem that the hybrids, the mulattoes, are all uniformly coffee-colored. But we know that this is in reality not so, because Mendelian segregation takes place. Although the average skin hue in mulattoes is intermediate between black and white, individuals with very light and with very dark skins are also born. Anyone who has observed the Negroes in the United States knows how tremendously they vary in their physical traits. Now, most of them are of course hybrids, descendants of persons of African and of European origin. Supposing that no more Negro-white crosses occur from now on, the American Negroes may eventually become a little more homogeneous than they are at present, but certainly nothing resembling complete uniformity will ever be reached. Some anthropologists consider this variable group a race in the making, designated as American Colored.

We can see where the old race notion went astray. It assumed, tactily or explicitly, that a race is a "community of blood." If that were so, the racial "ideal" obtained by averaging the characteristics of a group of peoples who have intermarried for generations would have some meaning: this "ideal" would approximately correspond to the type which would eventually be reached if this group were to continue intermarrying without any immigration from the outside. The heredity of any individual would be determined by the race from which he sprang. Every one of us would be, in a very real biological sense, blood of our race's blood and bone of our race's bone. The fact is, however, that every group of people consists of individuals who have certain genes in common but differ in other genes. Parents always differ in several, and probably in many genes. Their children differ in some genes both from their parents and from each other. The hereditary diversity of a group, be it a family, a clan, or a race, persists indefinitely. The heredity of an individual is only partly determined by the race from which he sprang. The diversity, the variation, found within a race is more important than the racial averages.

Definition of Race

People differ in the color of skin, eyes, hair, in stature, bodily proportions, and in many other traits. Each trait is determined by several, often by many, genes. How many variable genes there are in man is unknown; certainly hundreds, possibly thousands. Because of this, some of us have blue and others brown eyes, some have prominent and others flat noses, some are tall and others short. Such differences are, of course, common among people of the same country, state, town, members of a family, and even brothers and sisters. We do not suppose that every person with blue eyes belongs to a different race from everybody with brown eyes. It would be absurd to do so because blue and brown-eyed children are frequently born to the same parents. It happens, however, that certain genes are more frequent among the inhabitants of some countries than of others. Thus, blue eyes are very common in most parts of the United States but rather rare in most parts of Mexico. It is this and similar differences which make it possible to say that the inhabitants of the United States are in general racially distinct from the inhabitants of Mexico. Races can be defined as populations which differ in the frequencies of some gene or genes.

Blood Groups

Now let us try to understand the racial subdivision of mankind in the light of this definition. One of the most interesting human genes is that which determines the blood group to which each person belongs. It was of practical importance to work out the inheritance of this gene because of its relation to blood transfusion, the giving of blood by one person to another, so that the distribution of the varieties of this gene amongst the inhabitants of different parts of the world is now pretty well known. Our understanding of this whole question began in 1900 when Karl Landsteiner, then of Vienna, found the reason why blood transfusions from one person to another sometimes produced severe reactions of shock and sometimes even death of the recipient, while in other cases transfusion was successful. Landsteiner found that all human beings fall into four main groups according to the composition of their blood. The groups are known as O, A, B, and AB. Blood transfusion between members of the same group is safe. Blood from people of group O can safely be given to persons of any group, hence group O people are known as "universal donors." Persons of group AB are "universal recipients" since they can safely receive blood from any other person. But A blood can not be given safely to O or B persons, B blood should not be given to O or A persons while AB blood causes trouble when transfused into O, A or B persons. To which group you belong can be found out by drawing a drop of your blood and mixing it with some drops of blood serum (the fluid part of the blood from which the corpuscles have been removed) of persons known to be of group A and group B. If your blood corpuscles clump together or "agglutinate" in B serum, you belong to group A; if they clump in A serum, you belong to group B; if they clump in both A and B, you belong to group AB, while if no clumping takes place in either serum, you belong to group O. The whole examination takes only a few minutes and the clumping is perfectly clear under a microscope, or, with practice, it can be seen with the naked eye.

Genes and Geography

Within the last twenty to thirty years the blood groups of peoples in all parts of the world have been studied. The most interesting result of these studies has been that, with few exceptions, nearly every human group examined has been found to consist of a mixture of the *same* four blood groups; human races differ in the relative numbers of persons within them which fall into each of the four groups. Universal donors, group O, are found in every race and are generally the commonest type; group A is also common, while group B, and especially AB, is less common. The table below gives some idea of the frequency of the blood groups in different parts of the world.

The table shows that the same blood group genes are present, but in different proportions, in populations in different parts of the world. If we go from west to east in northern Europe, from Iceland to Russia, we find the proportion of people of group O steadily falling while that of group A tends to rise. From Finland to Siberia there is also a sharp rise in the proportion of group B, which reaches its world peak in Central Asia and Siberia. This gene is absent from the aboriginal populations of the Americas. The Eskimos, relatively recent arrivals in the New World, show very little of it. It is also absent in most Australian aborigines. African populations differ among themselves in their blood groups about as much as Europeans do. They differ from Europeans in other

PER CENTS OF PERSONS OF THE FOUR BLOOD GROUPS
AMONG THE INHABITANTS OF CERTAIN COUNTRIES

People	O	A	B	AB
EUROPE				
Iceland	56	32	10	2
Scotland	54	32	12	3
South England	43	45	8	4
Spain	42	47	9	2
Norway	40	49	8	3
Sweden	38	46	9	7
Finland	34	42	17	7
Sicily	46	34	17	3
Russia (Moscow)	32	34	25	9
ASIA				
Tartars	28	30	29	13
Kirghiz	32	27	32	9
Buriats	32	20	39	8
Chinese (Peking)	31	25	34	10
Japanese (Tokyo)	30	38	22	10

People	O	A	B	AB
NORTH AMERICA				
Eskimo	41	54	4	1
Navaho	75	25	....	....
Blackfeet	24	76	....	....
SOUTH AMERICA				
Toba (Argentina)	97	3	....	....
AFRICA				
Egyptians (Cairo)	27	39	25	9
Ethiopians	38	33	21	8
Congo Pygmies	31	30	29	10
Nigerians	57	19	19	5
AUSTRALIA				
Aborigines (W. Australia)	48	52	....	....

genes which influence the blood grouping. For example, when examined for another blood group system, known as Rh, Africans south of the Sahara show very high frequencies of one gene (Rh_0) which is extremely rare in Europe.

The most important lesson we can learn from this is that the races differ in blood group type only in a relative way. There are no absolute differences in which one race is all of one blood type, and another all of another type. Consider what this means. Suppose your blood is group O, that you are wounded and need a blood transfusion, and that many persons have offered to donate their blood, whom should you choose as a blood donor? The old and obsolete theory of heredity, and the ideas about race based upon it, would counsel you that a blood most similar to yours would be found in a person of the same race, and particularly in your close relatives, brothers or sisters. You may also hear that you should choose as blood donor a person of upright character and good disposition otherwise you may be contaminated by bad blood.

But you had better disregard such advice. If your

brother has A, B, or AB blood the transfusion would probably be fatal to you because his corpuscles would clump in your blood and clog the small blood vessels. On the other hand, a native of any land who possesses blood of group O will be a better donor regardless of his race or moral qualities. It is wiser to choose your donor according to his blood type, which is determined by his individual heredity, than according to the race from which he sprang. It is this property of his blood that matters, not his skin color, intelligence, or morals. By analogy, if you wish to hear good music it is wise to choose an artist who is a good musician; his blood group does not matter, nor is his skin color relevant. When you vote in a political election, the intelligence and honesty of the candidate, not his blood group or musical abilities, are relevant.

The Relativity of Race

The above conclusions sound pretty sweeping. Is it possible that they don't apply to characters other than the blood groups? While it is true that the blood groups are unusually clear and simple hereditary characters, they are not at all exceptional, since genes responsible for other traits show the same kind of distribution over the face of the earth. Take the first human gene difference mentioned in this book, the one which determines whether you can taste phenyl-thio-carbamide or not. This difference has been found in every human population which has been tested; so far as known, every race consists of tasters and non-tasters in proportions which are characteristic for the country but differ somewhat from country to country. The same is true of the gene for color-blindness, which is found in persons who cannot distinguish red from green. This crops out in every race, albeit with somewhat different frequencies. The same experience is repeated with genes for other blood characters, for various hereditary diseases and many other conditions.

It looks as though the whole human race had got its genes from the same source. One can imagine a huge aquarium tank in which a great variety of differently colored fish are swimming. There comes an order for fish to populate an aquarium in Utah and the shopkeeper dips his net and brings it up full of flashing fishes—many gold, some silver, a few black, some with fantails, some plain and many other kinds in different quantities. From this collection, there is established a population in a Salt Lake City pool, which may eventually be known as the Salt Lake City race. In response to a request from Buenos Aires the net dips in again and comes up with another collection, containing many of the same kinds as went to Salt Lake City, but in somewhat different proportions, lacking entirely a few of the rarer kinds but containing one or two different rare ones. Moreover in Argentina it turns out that the customers, naturally enough, like silver fish, so these are bred in larger numbers than the others and the proportions of the original sample are changed further. Everyone can recognize that the fish of the Salt Lake City pool and the inhabitants of the aquarium in Buenos Aires all came from the same source and that many of the same colors and kinds are found in each population, but the kind of mixture is distinctive for each "race" of fish. The original pool of course represents the collection of genes from which our ancestors and we of our particular race received our own particular sample of genes.

This same kind of distribution seems to hold even for the more complex human traits which have been used by anthropologists in characterizing races. A favorite trait of this sort has been head shape. Heads do not vary, as blood types do, in sharply defined, alternative categories. The variations are continuous from very long and narrow to very short and broad, with all intermediate shapes, and the differences probably depend not on one or two but on many genes. Heads of all shapes, long, medium and round, occur in all European countries, just as the four blood types appear in all of them; and as in the blood types, the proportions of persons with the different head shapes vary from country to country and from district to district. Roundheads are common in Central Europe—from France, through southern Germany and northern Italy, to Czechoslovakia, southern Poland, Hungary, Yugoslavia and Albania. The inhabitants of the British Isles, most of Scandinavia, and the Baltic provinces of Russia are mostly longheads. Another region of longheadedness is found in the South—Portugal, Spain, southern Italy. Between these regions in which roundheads or longheads predominate, and also in most of Russia, the population is mostly intermediate in head shape. People with round and long heads are found also outside of Europe. As examples of roundheads there are Apache Indians in America, Tahitians in the South Seas, and many tribes in Central Asia and in Siberia. Among the longheads are many Eskimos in America, the Australian Blackfellows, many Africans, and some Indian tribes in Asia.

Now the reason should be apparent why different scientists who attempted to classify mankind emerged with such different collections of "races." It is because the genes for different human traits vary quite independently of one another. If we were to classify Europeans according to their blood groups, we would probably make a "Western race" embracing English, French, Portuguese, and Spanish, who have little blood group B, a "Middle race" with a moderate amount of B, and an "Eastern race" (Poles, Russians and Finns) in which group B is frequent. According to the shape of the head, we should rather distinguish a "Central European" race where roundheads predominate, and two longheaded races—a "Northern" and a "Southern." It is not immediately evident why one of these classifications should be preferred to the other.

Taking mankind as a whole, the usual coloration of the hair is black, of the eyes dark brown, and of the skin more or less brown. It is only in Europe, and particularly across the northern part, from England, through Scandinavia and northern Germany to most of European Russia, that there is a large center of "blondness." From there these fair-skinned people have within the last few centuries spread all over the world. Southward and eastward from the northern countries the proportions of individuals with blue eyes, blond hair, and fair skin decrease and of those with brown eyes, brown or black hair, and swarthy skin increase. The "Dark Continent," Africa, is, of course, the world's center of dark pigmentation, although some of the natives of South Africa have again lighter skins. Asia and America are realms of yellow, brown, and "red" skin colors, although in some parts of Asia (southern India) and in Melanesia (New Guinea) the skin colors approach black.

The distribution of stature (height of the body) agrees neither with that of the blood groups, nor with that of the head shape or coloration, and we find a still different distribution if we study other physical features such as nose shape or ear form. It is easy to see then that the distribution of the genes which determine human "racial" traits over the earth's surface is very complex, and that different genes vary independently. Where does this leave the problem of the races of man? Well, the attempts to subdivide mankind neatly into several hard and fast racial compartments evidently have failed. They were based on false premises—on the belief in the "blood" theory of heredity. The sooner this fallacy is recognized for what it is, the better. But do not jump to the conclusion that mankind does not consist of races. The trouble is precisely that there are too many different races of too many different kinds.

Races are populations whch differ in the relative commonness of some of their genes. If we make a careful study of the populations not only of different countries but even of provinces or districts of the same country, in fact of neighboring villages, we shall almost certainly find them somewhat different. In one village there will be relatively more brunets and in the other more blonds; in one district the universal blood donors will be more frequent than in the other. The populations of these villages or districts are different races by the above definition, but you will never be certain from which village an individual came by merely looking at him or by examining his blood. On the other hand, it is easy to distinguish individuals of Central African from those of Central European parentage. All sorts of situations intermediate between these extremes also occur. If a group of people, some of them of Norwegian and others of Italian descent are present in the same room and you are asked to tell which is which, you will probably guess mostly right but you will make some mistakes too. In short, when we say that two populations are racially different we are not saying very much. They may be so different that it is possible to tell to which of them any individual belongs, or so similar that only very careful study by specialists can reveal their distinctness at all.

How Many Races?

In practice, scientists and laymen alike try to designate as races only populations the differences between which are large enough to be more or less easily recognizable. Small differences are simply ignored. But difficulties still remain. What may seem a small difference to you, may seem large to someone else. As we have seen, some scientists divided mankind into several dozen races and others into only two. It is quite futile, for example, to discuss whether or not Norwegians and Italians belong to the same race. Races merge into each other geographically. If we travel from Norway southward, through Germany, Switzerland, and Italy, we find that blue-eyed individuals become gradually less, and brown-eyed more, frequent. But nowhere is there a break or a divide on the two sides of which people are suddenly so different that we can say that here the northern race ends and the southern one begins. If we make not two but three races, a northern, a central, and a southern, the difficulty becomes even greater because instead of one indefinite boundary we have two hazy boundaries to contend with.

Only rarely can a more or less definite and not quite arbitrary line be drawn between the territories occupied by different races. This happens when their territories are separated from each other by some natural obstacle such as a desert or a mountain range, which impedes the movement of people from one territory to the other. Suppose that we continue our voyage southward from Norway beyond Italy. As we cross the Mediterranean Sea, the inhabitants of North Africa prove to be rather distinct from the Italians, although they still belong to the Mediterranean branch of the white race. Further southward lies the desert of Sahara, the crossing of which used to be a difficult undertaking; as a matter of fact, it still is difficult, except with the aid of an airplane. Now, as soon as the Sahara is crossed, we find peoples whose skin colors are strikingly darker than in those living north of the desert. We have left the territory of the white, and have arrived in the land of the black race.

Unfortunately for those who like cut-and-dried classifications and neat racial labels, human races are not usually separated by natural barriers such as the Sahara desert. Wherever the territories of two or more races come into direct contact, populations that are intermediate or that combine the traits of the races in question are found. The longer such contacts last in time the more widely spread the intermediate populations, and the more blurred become racial divisions. Eventually, a situation is reached when, as in Europe, one can recognize anything from a single race to a dozen or more races.

One should not conclude, however, that because the dividing lines between races are frequently arbitrary, races are imaginary entities. By looking at a suburban landscape one can not always be sure where the city begins and the country ends, but it does not follow from this that the city exists only in imagination. Races exist regardless of whether we can easily define them or not. It is a plain fact that most Norwegians can be told apart from most southern Italians by appearance, and this is true regardless of whether or not you decide to call them different races. Whatever your decision on this score, remember that differences between races are compounded from the kind of differences that are found between individuals of the same race. A Norwegian may carry some genes, and show some physical traits, which are typically "Italian," in the sense that they are more commonly met with in Italian than in Norwegian populations. A child born of parents of a given race does not necessarily possess all the traits which are usually met with in representatives of that race. The personal qualities of an individual are more important than the race from which he came.

Let us make very sure that we understand clearly why race boundaries are sharp if an obstacle to travel lies between the lands of these races, and become indefinite where the races come into contact. When people visit each other's homes or countries, they learn to know, to understand, and usually to like each other. One of the consequences is increased frequency of intermarriage. This, the old biologists and anthropologists thought, leads to mixture of the "bloods" of the races, and appearance of intermediate or mixed racial groups. Although the "blood" theory of heredity is wrong, the view that intermarriage between races leads to their eventual fusion into a single variable group is correct. Suppose that one race has 90 per cent of individuals with blue and 10 per cent with brown eyes, and another race has 10 per cent blue-eyed and 90 per cent brown-eyed individuals. If representatives of these races intermarry, the number of couples in which one party has blue and the other brown eyes will be greater than if marriages take place only between members of the same race. Of course, no mixing or fusion of the genes for the blue and the brown eye colors takes place in the hybrids. What will happen, however, is that brown-eyed individuals will be commoner than they were in the predominantly blue-eyed race, and blue-eyed individuals will be commoner than they were in the predominantly brown-eyed race. If intermarriage continues long enough the proportions of the blue- and brown-eyed individuals will become alike in both populations—that is the two races will be merged into one.

This kind of mixing does not mean the loss of identity

of the elements, that is the genes, which give the race its character. In fact, it is just this durability of the genes through all the mixing of races which has gone on throughout human history, that makes possible, today, the separation of races as groups differing in the frequency of certain genes. One can liken this integrity of the genes to the stubbornness with which chemical elements retain all of their individual properties regardless of the succession of combinations into which they enter, or to the recovery of each pack of differently marked cards after a game in which several packs have been merged into a single stock.

Human races differ usually in many genes and many traits. Intermarriage pushes the frequencies of all these genes toward equality in both races. Suppose that most individuals of one race are blue-eyed, longheaded and tall, and of the other race brown-eyed, roundheaded and short. The "mixed race" which will emerge after continued intermarriage will show a great diversity of physical types. There will be individuals with blue and with brown eyes, with long, intermediate, and round heads, tall, intermediate and short in stature. There will arise individuals having combinations of traits which seldom or never were found in the original races, such as the combination of blue eyes, round head and intermediate or tall stature. Negroes in the United States are a "mixed race" descended through intermarriage of representatives of many tribes which lived originally in various parts of Africa and of several strains of white people from Europe. The skin color of American Negroes varies from black to a shade as pale as can be found among "pure" whites; the nose shape from extremely flat to very prominent; hair from tightly curled to almost straight; stature from giant to dwarf, etc.

If all peoples on earth were to intermarry at random, the resulting humanity would not, as is frequently but mistakenly supposed, be some kind of a compromise between all the now existing races. It would rather be an extremely variable lot: some persons resembling each of the now existing races would continue to be born, but other individuals would have combinations of traits that are rare or non-existent at present.

The present racial subdivisions of mankind owe their continued persistence to the fact that marriages between members of different races are less frequent than marriages within the races. People tend to marry members of their own race for several reasons. The most important reason is a geographical one. It is obvious that the chance of a boy born in New York marrying a New York girl is greater than the chance of his marrying a girl from any other town in the United States, not to mention other countries. The importance of distance in human life, however, progressively declines as civilization develops. As men learned to travel, first on foot and then by canoe, on horseback, by covered wagon, ship, train, automobile and airplane, marriages of persons born in different parts of a country and even in remote parts of the world became more and more frequent. The exchange of genes between the previously segregated races has increased hand in hand with the conquest of space. There is no doubt that civilization leads slowly but inexorably toward breakdown of race divisions.

Races of Man and Breeds of Animals

Although putting racial labels on human populations is an arbitrary procedure, it is a fact that the human species is not homogeneous but consists of subdivisions of various orders which differ from each other in the relative commonness of many genes. Biologically, these subdivisions are quite analagous to the races or sub-species of animals or plants in nature, and to the breeds or varieties of domesticated animals and cultivated plants. All of these arise in the course of evolution through the occurrence of mutations, gene recombination, and natural or artificial selection of those collections of genes which are suited to certain environments.

And yet, races of man also have characteristics which distinguish them from races of other animals. Men are subject not only to biological but also to social forces, and these two kinds of influences are in continual interaction with each other.

While races of wild animals and plants are kept apart by geographical separation alone, human races may be isolated by cultural barriers. Civilized as well as primitive men have certain rules which govern the choice of mates and these rules frequently prescribe marital unions within a specified group—a clan, a tribe, nation, religious denomination, economic or social circle. This permits different racial groups to coexist side by side, at least for a time, in the same country.

In the same territory, human racial groups may remain relatively distinct, whereas in wild animals and plants which reproduce sexually, usually no more than a single race of a species is found in one locality. The castes of India are the most striking examples of this. Members of a caste are supposed to, and practically always do, marry within their caste. Some of the castes are descended from racially different peoples who invaded India from beyond its borders at various times during its long history. Others appear to have separated more recently and to be kept apart by marriage customs.

Considered biologically, the idea of Negro-white segregation as propounded by partisans of this measure in the United States is a plan to prevent the flow of genes between these races by social means—custom and legislation—instead of by geographical separation. Milder forms of social barriers against intermarriage of groups of peoples, such as religious, economic, educational and language divisions, may also slow down the gene exchange between populations and postpone for a time the obliteration of the races. But the long time trend is clearly toward race fusion.

Contrary to the opinion vociferously expressed by some sincere but misguided people, such a trend is not biologically dangerous. Mixing of closely related races may even lead to increased vigor. As for the most distantly separated races, there is no basis in fact to think that either biological stimulation or deterioration follows crossing. The widespread belief that human race hybrids are inferior to both of their parents and somehow constitutionally unbalanced must be counted among the superstitions.

Do Human Races Differ in Mental Capacity?

Breeds of dogs differ markedly in temperament, in responsiveness to particular kinds of training, and hence in the uses to which they may best be put by man. Although almost any dog can be trained when young to be of some use, one would not, for choice, try to train a dachshund to be a sheepherder, or a shepherd dog to hunt rabbits. Similarly, the differences in temperament between polo ponies and draft horses, which are certainly conditioned in part by their heredity, fit them for different functions. These breed differences have been accentuated by selective breeding by men who had these different functions in view. It has often been argued by analogy that differences in biological heredity lie at the bottom of intellectual, emotional, and temperamental differences between races and between cultural and social groups.

Another argument runs as follows: Races arise as a part of the evolutionary process, by which populations within a species become adapted to a particular environment. Racial variation in skin color has, for example, been viewed in this way. If biological evolution has caused races of man to diverge in physical characters, should it not have done the same for the mental capacities and aptitudes of these people?

Both of these arguments by analogy are unconvincing, because they are based on a misunderstanding of the nature of biological heredity. It has been pointed out repeatedly in this book that what is inherited is not this or that trait, but the manner in which the developing organism responds to its environment. Now, the amount as well as the kind of variation which a trait shows in different environments is decided by the hereditary make-up of the organism. For example, individuals who carry the genes for the O, A, or B blood groups have the respective blood groups regardless of their state of health, the climate they live in, or the nutrition which they receive. The blood group is rigidly fixed by heredity. But the skin color is not so rigidly fixed, since it can change rather rapidly depending upon the exposure of the skin to sunlight. Finally, whether or not an individual gets into conflicts with the law depends upon the person's upbringing and circumstances, and also upon the kind of laws which the society sees fit to establish. Human behavior is, then, quite plastic and can be changed by the living conditions.

The important problem is why some traits are more and others less fixed or plastic. The fixity or plasticity of a trait is a matter of evolutionary adaptation. By and large, the traits which are important for the survival in all the environments which a species or a race normally encounters are fixed; the development of the organism is so "buffered" against external disturbances that the trait almost invariably appears. Thus, man is almost always born with and grows up having the same set of internal organs, of physiological functions, and with a capacity to reason and to learn from experience.

But it is also advantageous for the safety of the organism to have some traits change rather easily when the environment changes. For example, dark skin pigmentation is advantageous during summer vacation on the seashore. But little skin pigment is supposedly advantageous to secure a supply of vitamin D (the "sunlight" vitamin) when sunlight is scarce. The genetic constitution which is most favorable in a changeable climate is, then, one which permits the development of darker or lighter skin colors at different seasons and in different climates.

The relative fixity of the temperamental make-up of horse or dog breeds is, then, understandable. These breeds have been fashioned by man and intended for different uses. A great Dane with the temper of a fox terrier might be dangerous, and a fox terrier with the temperament of a great Dane would be boring. The

genetic component is important in the temperament of
these breeds. It has been made important by selection
and breeding. But has there been a similar selection in
the evolution of man?

It is obvious that different social positions and different trades call for somewhat different behavior patterns.
The qualities most useful in a military leader are not the
same which are most favored in a writer or a scientist,
and vice versa. The mentality of a nomadic hunter is
usually different from that of a farmer. But the pre-
eminent requirement of living in any human society is
very nearly always the same: it is the ability to learn
from experience and to adjust one's behavior to the
needs and circumstances. This requirement is fundamental for living in any culture or civilization, from the
most primitive to the most complex. Accordingly, the
process of selection which has been, and still is, most
powerful and persistent in human evolution is that for
the ability to learn new ways of behavior, new techniques
of doing things, and new skills.

In short, the human species as a whole has developed
away from genetic specialization and fixity of behavior,
and toward educability. This is true for all races of man
and for all climates. Therein lies the most important
biological feature of the evolutionary pattern of mankind. Breeds of dogs or of horses have been deliberately
fashioned for performance of different services by making
their genes different. Man is certainly capable of pur-
suing a great variety of ways of life. But he is enabled
to do so by different training and education, not by ac-
quiring different genes. This does not mean that the
genetic differences among men do not affect their mentality. But from the vantage point of evolutionary biology
we can see that such differences are not fundamental. Far
more important is the fact that human capacities are
developed by training from childhood on. Pathological
cases aside, human personality is shaped mainly by the
patterns of interpersonal relations which prevail in a
given culture, and by the individual experiences of each
member of a community. This genetically conditioned

educability has guaranteed the success of mankind as a biological species, and has, in turn, permitted progressively more advanced cultural developments.

Concluding Remarks

Although universal uniformity of men appeals to some people, there is no reason why monotonous sameness should be our goal. On the contrary, such a prospect appears bleak in the extreme. Psychological and cultural differences among individuals and groups furnish the leaven of creative effort which carries mankind toward ever greater achievements. The question of whether or not human races differ in hereditary psychological traits for the time being must be regarded as open. We know that a variety of different civilizations have existed and exist in the world. The differences between them certainly can not be accounted for by the biological differences between the groups of people who created, developed, and maintained these civilizations. The differences between the so-called "race psychologies" are determined by the cultural differences to an extent assuredly greater than they may be influenced by biological heredity. Furthermore, psychic differences between individuals are certainly much greater than the average differences between nations or races.

We have seen that the psychic trait which has been, and still is, most favored in human evolution is the ability to profit from experience, the educability. Now, educability does not make all men alike. The exact opposite is true. The survival advantage of the ability to learn and to be trained consists precisely in that the development of a person can be turned in any one of many possible directions, as necessity may demand. Educability permits, then, a vastly greater diversity of human personalities than could possibly arise if human mentality were genetically fixed, as it is, for example, in the inhabitants of the anthill. Far from fostering mental uniformity, human evolution has led to increasing diversity.

Regardless of how the problem of the relations between biological heredity, individual and group psychology, and culture may eventually be settled, the variety of human cultures will appear to us an inspiration rather than a curse if we learn to respect, to understand, and to admire them. In the realm of culture there is enough room to accommodate the diversified contributions not only of different individuals but also of every nation and race. It is a waste of time to discuss which particular contributions are superior and which inferior. There is no common measure applicable to the works of a poet, an artist, a philosopher, a scientist, and the simple kindness of heart of a plain man. Humanity needs them all.

Appendix

Why Do the Proportions of Dominant and Recessive Genes in a Population Remain Constant from Generation to Generation?

SUPPOSE THAT a previously uninhabited island or other unoccupied and isolated tract of land is populated by a group of immigrants among whom there are as many individuals who can as those who can not taste the PTC substance. The ability to taste PTC is, as we know, due to the gene T, the inability to taste it to the gene t. Suppose that the tasters are all pure (homozygous) for the gene T (TT). This gene, T, for tasting is dominant to that for non-tasting, t, and the non-tasters are always pure for that gene (tt). What proportions of tasters and non-tasters will be found in the population of the island in the next and in all following generations? Since it does not matter for people whether or not they can or can not taste PTC, and in fact very few people know to which of these two categories they belong, the ability or inability to taste this substance will not affect the marriage choices among the immigrants. In other words, the chances that a taster will marry another taster or a non-taster will be determined simply by the proportions of the tasters and non-tasters among the eligible mates. If so, the married couples and their progenies will be about as follows:

MARRIAGES		Proportions of the	
Man	Wife	marriages	Children
TT (taster)	TT (taster)	25%	TT (tasters)
TT (taster)	tt (non-taster)		Tt (tasters)
tt (non-taster)	TT (taster)	50%	Tt (tasters)
tt (non-taster)	tt (non-taster)	25%	tt (non-tasters)

Of the men who are tasters, about half will marry tasters and half non-tasters; of the men who are non-tasters about half will marry tasters and half non-tasters. This means that of all marriages about ¼ involve both tasters, about ½ are "mixed marriages" and in about ¼ both partners are non-tasters. If tasters and non-tasters live about equally long and have about the same number of children, the first generation of children will consist of ¼ pure tasters *TT*, ½ hybrid tasters *Tt,* and ¼ pure non-tasters *tt,* or in other words about 75 per cent tasters and 25 per cent non-tasters.

Now we want to know what kind of children *these* children will have if marriages amongst them take place at random with respect to the ability to taste PTC. In this case there will be three kinds of men (*TT, Tt* and *tt*) and the same three kinds of women in the proportion ¼:½:¼. The possible combinations of husbands and wives and the children expected from these marriages, if four children are born from each marriage, will be as follows:

Men	Wives	Proportion of the marriages	Children		
¼ *TT*	¼ *TT*	¹⁄₁₆	4 *TT*		
¼ *TT*	½ *Tt*	²⁄₁₆	4 *TT*	4 *Tt*	
¼ *TT*	¼ *tt*	¹⁄₁₆		4 *Tt*	
½ *Tt*	¼ *TT*	²⁄₁₆	4 *TT*	4 *Tt*	
½ *Tt*	½ *Tt*	⁴⁄₁₆	4 *TT*	8 *Tt*	4 *tt*
½ *Tt*	¼ *tt*	²⁄₁₆		4 *Tt*	4 *tt*
¼ *tt*	¼ *TT*	¹⁄₁₆		4 *Tt*	
¼ *tt*	½ *Tt*	²⁄₁₆		4 *Tt*	4 *tt*
¼ *tt*	¼ *tt*	¹⁄₁₆			4 *tt*
		Totals	16 *TT*	32 *Tt*	16 *tt*

The children will again appear in the proportion ¼ *TT* ½ *Tt* ¼ *tt*. There will have been no change in the ratio of tasters to non-tasters. They will remain just as common as they were among the parents.

The same conclusion can be reached in a different way. Instead of considering the random mating among the members of the population, we can think of the genes which are transmitted through eggs and sperm as constituting a great pool from which two genes, one from the mother and one from the father, are drawn out whenever a new individual is formed. In the original mixture there were equal numbers of T and t genes. When these are drawn out two at a time, we find that two T's are drawn about once every four draws, two t's also once in four times while a T and t appear twice in each four draws. So we come again to the conclusion that the first generation will consist of 25 per cent $T \cdot T$ (pure tasters), 50 per cent Tt (hybrid tasters) and 25 per cent tt (non-tasters).

But what will the second, third and later generations of the islanders be like? Consider again the pool of genes in the sex cells which will give rise to the next generation. The 25 pure tasters TT will have contributed 50 cells, each with T; the 25 non-tasters will give 50 cells each with t. The 50 hybrid tasters (Tt) will contribute 100 cells, 50 of them with T and 50 with t. The whole pool will have 100 T and 100 t, that is, equal numbers of the two kinds of gene, just the same as the pool from which the first generation arose. This means that the second generation, like the first, will consist of

$$\left. \begin{array}{l} 25 \text{ per cent } TT \\ 50 \text{ per cent } Tt \end{array} \right\} \text{ tasters}$$
$$25 \text{ per cent } tt \quad \text{non-tasters}$$

All the following generations will be like the first and second, and the pool will always contain about equal numbers of T and t sex cells. The proportions of tasters and non-tasters established in the first generation will persist indefinitely, as long as people marry without regard to their ability or inability to taste PTC. The dominant gene T will neither crowd out the recessive t nor will it be crowded out by t. The proportion of the two kinds of gene remains constant. They are "in equilibrium."

An island with just half tasters and half non-tasters is

a rather special case; but it is not difficult to prove that the proportions of a pair of genes will remain constant regardless of what the proportion is. Suppose, for example, that the original pool consisted of 90 per cent T and 10 per cent t sex cells. If $\frac{9}{10}$ of the sex cells have T and $\frac{1}{10}$ have t, then when we draw them out two at a time, each T will have nine chances of meeting a T and one chance of meeting a t; each t will also have nine chances of meeting a T to one chance of meeting a t. Therefore 81 per cent (9 times 9) of all combinations, thence of all people arising from such fertilized eggs, will have two T genes; 18 per cent (9 times 1 taken twice) will have a T and a t, and one per cent (one times one) will have two t genes. The generation arising from such random mating will therefore consist of:

$$\left. \begin{array}{l} 81 \text{ per cent } TT \\ 18 \text{ per cent } Tt \end{array} \right\} \text{ tasters}$$
$$1 \text{ per cent } tt \qquad \text{non-tasters}$$

If each of these contributes two genes to the pool from which the genes of the next generation will be drawn, the pure tasters will contribute 162 T sex cells, the hybrid tasters 18 T and 18 t sex cells, and the non-tasters 2 t sex cells. The totals are 180 T and 20 t or a ratio of 90 per cent T to 10 per cent t. Since this is the same as the original proportion, the second and all the following generations will continue to have 99 per cent of tasters and 1 per cent of non-tasters.

The proportions of the genes will remain constant indefinitely regardless of what their original proportions may be. For those who are not afraid of first year algebra, here is the proof of this statement. Suppose that a fraction q of the sex cells of the original settlers carry the gene T, and a fraction (1-q) the gene t. The first generation of islanders will, then, consist of: $q^2TT + 2q (1\text{-}q) Tt + (1\text{-}q)^2 tt = 1$. The "poor" of sex cells of the next generation will contain $q^2 + q (1\text{-}q) = q$ cells with T, and $q (1\text{-}q) + (1\text{-}q)^2 = (1\text{-}q)$ cells with t. Obviously, the relative frequencies of T and t remain constant. Using the proportions of tasters and non-tasters in the United States 70 per cent to 30 per cent, we can derive a value of $(1-q)^2 = .30$; $(1-q) = .547$; $q = .453$, that is the "American pool" of genes consists of about 45 per cent T and 55 per cent t, and this remains constant generation after generation, provided no immigrants with different proportions of T and t enter to disturb the gene frequency and that mutation does not favor either T or t.

Any other pair of genes will behave in the same way as T and t provided the population is large and there is random mating. This allows us to predict what will happen in human populations.

INDEX

141